SUPER FORMULAS

Arts and Crafts

**How to make
more than 360 useful products
that contain honey and beeswax.**

by
Elaine C. White

VALLEY HILLS PRESS
Starkville, Mississippi

Super Formulas, Arts and Crafts

The information in this book has been carefully researched, and all efforts have been made to ensure accuracy. Valley Hills Press assumes no responsibility for any injuries suffered or damages or losses incurred during the use of, or as a result of following, this information. All directions should be carefully studied and clearly understood before taking any action based on the information and advice presented in this book.

Manufactured in the United States of America
Production supervision by Quail Ridge Press/Post Office Box 123/Brandon MS 39043
Cover design by William Pitts/815 Reaves Street/Jackson MS 39204
1st printing 3,000 - May, 1993
2nd printing 3,000 - December, 1993

Publisher's Cataloging in Publication
(Prepared by Quality Books Inc.)

White, Elaine C.
Super formulas, arts and crafts : how to make more than 360 useful products that contain honey and beeswax / by Elaine C. White.
p. cm.
Includes index.
Preassigned LCCN: 93-93807.
ISBN 0-9637539-7-5

1. Bee products. 2. Honey. 3. Beeswax. I. Title.

SF539.W45 1993 638.16'028
QBI93-1268

The Author

Elaine White is a house-wife and beekeeper who lives in central Mississippi with husband, Wil, and son, John. Her passion for formulas and ways to use beeswax and honey led to years of research and testing. Wil encouraged Elaine to organize her notes on a computer and ***Super Formulas, Arts and Crafts*** is the result. Parts of this book have appeared in *Bee Culture* and *Countryside* magazines and the *American Bee Journal.* Elaine hopes you enjoy sharing "the passion."

This book is dedicated

to Marilyn Thompson,
who introduced me to beekeeping;

to Harry Fulton and Clarence Collison,
my favorite beekeeping instructors;

and to my husband, Wil, and son, John, for their
help with the computer and for their patience the nights
I made formulas instead of dinner.

CONTENTS

ADHESIVES

WATERPROOF CEMENT

This old-fashioned, waterproof cement is formulated to hold blades onto knife handles. This formula was often used for aquariums and to join marble to wood.

Ounces by weight:
1/2 ounce beeswax
1 ounce plaster of Paris
4 ounces rosin

Heat the beeswax in a microwave until it melts and add the rosin. Microwave, stirring every 30 seconds, until the rosin melts. Stir in the plaster of Paris. Heat the handle end of a knife blade over a flame and cover it with the hot cement. Insert the blade into the handle, wipe off excess cement and leave the knife undisturbed to cool.

This cement may be cast into sticks and later heated for use on metal, wood or glass. Parts to be joined should be warm.

ENVELOPE GLUE

This is a moistening-type glue for stamps, labels or the flaps of envelopes. Also see page 101 for "Moisten-to-Seal Glue".

1 tablespoon gum Arabic
1/2 cup water
1 tablespoon laundry starch
1/4 cup honey
1/4 teaspoon wintergreen essential oil
(See "Essential Oils" page 28.)

Heat the ingredients in a double boiler for 15 minutes. Add the wintergreen essential oil if it is desired to improve the taste. With a brush, apply a very thin coat of the hot glue to paper and allow it to dry. Moisten the glue to seal the envelope or attach labels.

When stored in a jar and allowed to cool, this glue thickens and can be used as a normal paper paste. Gum Arabic and oil of wintergreen are sold by herb suppliers such as "Penn Herb" (see Appendix A).

METAL LEAF ADHESIVE

This easily formulated paste is used to apply gold, silver, or copper metal leaf onto wood, plaster, glass, or metal.

5 measures beeswax
1 measure Canada balsam

Melt the ingredients in a microwave or a double boiler. Allow the paste to cool slightly. Apply the thick paste to wood or plaster. Rub it thoroughly onto the surface so that no part is untouched. Use a rag dampened with turpentine to rub down the surface and obtain an even layer of adhesive.

Lay the metal leaf directly onto the paste and press it down firmly with a ball of absorbent cotton. Wait one day. Brush off the excess metal leaf with a clean, dry sable brush. Canada balsam and beeswax are sold by "Chem Lab." Metal leaf is sold by wood-finishing suppliers such as "Woodworker's Supply" and by artist's suppliers (Appendix A).

STICKY WAX--See page 13.

ARTHRITIS

Warm wax treatments are approved by the Arthritis Foundation to help relieve sore, painful joints caused by arthritis. Wax treatments provide moist heat, increase blood circulation, and ease stiffness due to joint inflammation.

Researchers at Sahlgren University Hospital in Gothenburg, Sweden evaluated the effects of hand exercise and warm wax treatment in 52 people with rheumatoid arthritis in the hands. Participants in the study were randomly assigned to one of four groups: one group received wax-bath treatment followed by active hand exercise, one received hand exercise only, one received wax treatment only, and the fourth received no treatment. Certain variables such as range of motion, grip function, pain and stiffness were evaluated in each of the groups before and after the four-week treatment period.

At the conclusion of the study, the greatest improvement in range of motion and grip function was seen in the group receiving both wax treatments and exercise. Hand exercise alone also reduced stiffness and pain. Wax baths alone had no significant effect. The researchers conclude that wax treatments provide quick, short-term pain relief. They believe this short-term relief makes it easier for people to exercise, which can improve function.

The mission of the Arthritis Foundation is to support research to find the cure for and prevention of arthritis and to improve the quality of life for those affected by arthritis.

For arthritis information contact:

Arthritis Foundation
Post Office Box 19000
Atlanta, Georgia 30326
1-800-283-7800

WARM WAX TREATMENT

5 pounds wax
2 cups mineral oil

Step 1: Melt the ingredients in an oven set between 170 to 200 degrees F. Stir to mix the oil and wax.

Step 2: Remove the mixture from the oven and allow it to cool until there is a film of cooled wax on the surface (about 125 degrees F.). Test the wax to be sure it is very warm, but not uncomfortable.

Step 3: The body part treated must be clean and dry. Dip the body part into the wax mixture and withdraw it. If the hand is being treated, keep the fingers apart. Do this a few more times until there is a thick coating of wax.

Step 4: Return the body part to the wax and leave it there (15 to 30 minutes) until the mixture cools.

Step 5: Remove the body part and peel off the wax. Save the wax in a closed container to use again. The treatment may be repeated. The mixture will melt more quickly now that the oil and wax are combined.

ART MEDIUMS

Mediums are combinations of ingredients suitable for adding to (or combining with) paint or pigments. Beeswax combines well with resins and oils. Its permanence has been known for centuries. It reduces some of the high gloss of oil paints while thickening them to a buttery consistency.

The ingredients for this section are sold by artist's suppliers such as "Daniel Smith" (see Appendix A). Ingredients listed by measures means that any container can be used to measure them: teaspoons, tablespoons or small cans.

ENCAUSTIC PAINTING

See page 25.

OIL PAINT I

1 measure beeswax
3 measures turpentine

Melt the beeswax in a microwave or a double boiler. Remove it from the heat and stir in the turpentine.

For direct painting, combine the mixture on a palette with tube oil paint. Thin or thick coats can be applied over oil, tempera or glue paints. Use only a wax varnish over the finished painting.

OIL PAINT II

4 measures beeswax
1 measure Damar varnish
1 measure boiled linseed oil
12 measures turpentine

Heat the ingredients in a double boiler until they are combined. Remove the boiler from the heat and stir until the mixture forms a soft paste. Combine the soft paste on a palette with tube oil paints. Apply the paint as a final paint layer or glaze. Varnish the painting with a wax varnish only.

VARNISHES

Wax varnish is a soft finish that is impervious to most harmful atmospheric effects, yet it is easy to remove for cleaning or renewal of the painting. It provides a smooth, low-luster finish over any painting. (See page 103 for "Flat Varnish" for furniture.)

WAX VARNISH I

This final varnish produces a soft, low luster that dries within one hour.

8 measures beeswax
1 measure Damar varnish
1 measure boiled linseed oil
10 measures turpentine

Heat the ingredients in a double boiler until they are combined. Remove it from the heat and stir until the mixture cools. Apply the mixture thinly with a lint-free cloth, let it dry and polish it to a soft luster.

WAX VARNISH II

4 measures Damar varnish
2 measures beeswax
1 measure turpentine

Heat the ingredients in a double boiler until they are combined. Remove it from the heat and stir until the mixture cools.

Apply the mixture thinly with a lint-free cloth, let it dry and polish it with a cloth.

WAX VARNISH III

1/2 measure carnauba wax
1 measure beeswax
6 measures turpentine

Heat the ingredients in a double boiler until the wax melts. Remove it from the heat and stir until the mixture cools to a soft paste. Apply a thin coat of the varnish with a rag or brush, let it dry and polish it with a soft cloth.

WAX CRAYONS

Artists can create any color crayon desired. These crayons should not be used by children because some pigments are not food safe.

Parts by weight:
2 parts beeswax
1 part talc
Pigment

Melt the wax in a microwave or a small can placed in boiling water. Stir in the talc and dry artist's pigment or fresco colors. Pour the mixture into a lubricated aluminum foil mold. The crayon may be melted again and more pigment added until it is the exact color desired.

WAX EMULSION

This formula has the handling quality of a water medium and the permanence of a wax paint.

1 measure beeswax
8 measures water
2 measures household ammonia

Place the wax and water in a pan large enough to hold three times the volume to allow for foaming. Apply low heat until the wax melts. Stir in the ammonia a little at a time. If it threatens to foam over, remove it from the heat. Stir until the foam subsides. Let it cool.

Combine the formula with dry pigments and water. This can be used over paper, cardboard or canvas. When the paint has dried thoroughly, rub it to a soft luster with a dry cloth.

WAX PASTEL CRAYONS

Applications of this soft crayon can be blended the same as chalk pastels.

Parts by weight:
1 part grated soap
1 part beeswax
Pigment

Melt the beeswax in a small can placed in boiling water. Add the grated soap and stir until the soap melts and the mixture is smooth. Color the mixture with dry artist's pigments or fresco colors. Pour it into lubricated aluminum foil molds. After testing the crayon, it can be melted again and more pigment added. Since some pigments are not food safe, these crayons should not be used by children.

Wax Pastels for Children:
Follow the directions above for "Wax Pastel Crayons" using concentrated food coloring paste as the pigment. The paste is sold with cake decorating supplies. The crayons are food safe and they blend well. Their color is almost as concentrated as the crayons made with artist's pigment.

BATIK

Batik is a wax-resist method of dyeing fabric. Although the historic source is unknown, the art developed in the Orient, apparently in China or India. It was developed to a high degree in Java, where it is still practiced. The fluid, free-hand nature of batik enables the creative artist and the ordinary craftsperson to apply their skill. It is easy to combine batik with other methods of dyeing fabric, such as dye-painting and tie-dyeing.

EQUIPMENT AND SUPPLIES

The following are sold by "Earth Guild" (see Appendix A).

- ❑ Beeswax and paraffin
- ❑ *Tjanting* or *kiska* (wax-writing tools) (See page 6.)
- ❑ Cold-water fabric dye
- ❑ Silk or cotton fabric

GENERAL DIRECTIONS

Step 1: Wax penetrates thin fabrics more easily than thick ones. Use white or pastel-colored, 100% silk or cotton fabric. "Earth Guild" sells silk by the yard and silk scarves, hemmed and ready for batik. Wash the fabric to remove sizing. Dry the fabric and iron it smooth.

Step 2: Mount the fabric on a frame to hold it taut and to keep it from touching anything while it is being waxed. A picture frame works well or the open end of a wooden or cardboard box. Pin, staple or tape the fabric to the frame. The fabric is taken off and refastened each time it is dyed, so the fastening should not be too difficult to undo. Designs can be sketched on the fabric with charcoal or chalk.

Step 3: Line an electric skillet or griddle with aluminum foil to protect it. Set the temperature control at 300 degrees F. Place a large can in the skillet and 1 pound of beeswax in the can to melt (about 45 minutes). Crude beeswax (see page 83) can be used if it is strained through fine cheesecloth or a nylon stocking.

Step 4: Test the wax on a small piece of fabric. If the wax is too cool it will not penetrate the fabric. It will clump on top and show up as a yellowish-to-white crust. Check the back of the fabric. If the wax is too hot, it will run through the fabric and smear. Adjust the temperature until the wax flows properly.

Step 5: Apply melted wax to the surface of the fabric. Designs formed by this first waxing preserve the natural fabric color.

Step 6: Prepare cold-water fabric dye as the package directs. To hold the dye, use a flat, wide pan that is large enough that the fabric can be immersed without crumpling. If cracking effects are desired, intentionally crumple the fabric. Leave the fabric in the dye 15 minutes. Remove the fabric and rinse it under running water until the rinse water is clear. Hang the fabric to dry completely before going to the next step. Wax will not penetrate wet fabric.

Step 7: Attach dry fabric to the frame and repeat Steps 5 and 6. This application protects the color of the dye. Repeat Steps 5 and 6 as many times as desired.

Step 8: When the dye process is complete, boil the fabric to set the dye and to melt the wax. Do not pour the waxy water down the drain! Remove the fabric and allow the water to cool. The wax can be lifted from the pot, laid on towels to dry, and used again. Gently boil the fabric again in water with a little detergent added to remove more wax, or have the fabric dry cleaned.

WAX APPLICATION

Beeswax is pliable and prevents dye from penetrating fabric. Paraffin is more brittle. It cracks, and dye penetrates the cracks. Cracking forms interesting designs when the fabric is dyed. Vary the amount of paraffin combined with the beeswax to vary the cracking effects. Freeze or crumple the fabric to increase cracking, or use 100% beeswax for minimal cracking.

Wax may be applied by any method as long as the fabric is penetrated. "Earth Guild" and "Surma" (see Appendix A) sell beeswax and tjantings .

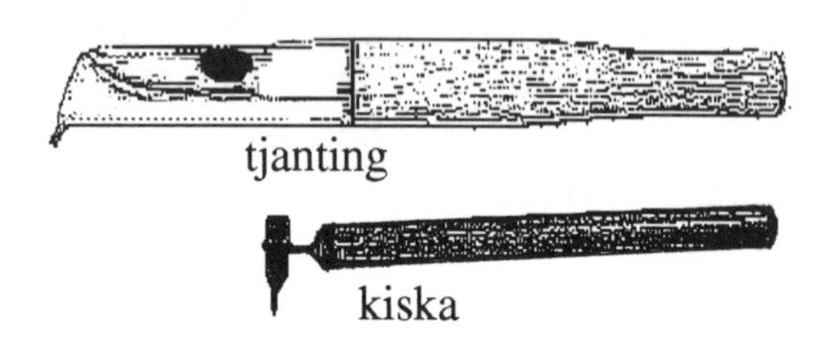

♦ A *tjanting* is a batik wax pen with a small bowl to hold melted wax and a tip to draw a fine line of wax over the fabric. A *kiska* is a smaller wax pen traditionally used to make "Ukrainian Easter Eggs" (see page 95). They are available in various sizes.

♦ Wax can be placed in an oil can. Set the can on the skillet to melt the wax and use the can as a wax applicator.

♦ Brushes cover wide areas and are good for thick lines and filling in shapes.

♦ Blocks, stamps and cookie cutters may be dipped into the melted wax and used to apply wax to the fabric.

♦ Pipe cleaners and strings may be dipped into wax and laid on the fabric.

♦ Wax can be dribbled onto the fabric from a burning candle.

♦ Electric wax funnel pens are sold by "Candlewic" (see Appendix A).

♦ Cut adhesive vinyl sheets into designs or form a stencil. Press the vinyl firmly onto dry, unwaxed fabric. Apply wax around or within the stencil. The vinyl keeps wax off the fabric. Remove the vinyl and dye the fabric. Stained glass suppliers (see Appendix A) sell adhesive vinyl already cut into beautiful designs.

DYES

Dyes for the batik method must be cold-water types in order not to melt the wax-resist. "Earth Guild" (see Appendix A) sells Procion MX dye that is good for batik. An understanding of colors and their relationships is an important part of batik. It is also the part that gives the greatest pleasure and variety to the craft. Most batik is done in 2 to 4 colors of a color family, beginning with the lightest color and ending with the darkest. The following are examples:

♦ Yellow, golden yellow, orange and scarlet;

♦ Light blue, evening blue, royal blue and navy blue;

♦ Light green, kelly green, forest green, and dark green;

♦ Pink, rose pink, scarlet and cardinal red;

♦ White, ecru, tan and cocoa brown.

The original fabric color and dyeing one color over another influences the resulting color. The color charts below and on page 17 are quite helpful.

If the Fabric is:	Dye It:	To Get:
Bright yellow	Red	Deep orange
Red	Blue	Purple
Blue	Red	Purple
Light blue	Pink	Lavender
Yellow	Blue	Green
Green	Yellow	Lime green
Green	Blue	Aqua
Medium brown	Green	Olive drab
Purple	Navy blue	Plum
Orange	Tan	Burnt orange
Tan	Rose pink	Rose beige
Red	Dark green	Black
Green	Scarlet	Black
Brown	Navy blue	Black

DYE PAINTING

Instead of immersing the fabric in dye, use a paint brush to fill in wax-outlined designs with concentrated dye. A squeeze bottle of concentrated dye can also be used to apply color within waxed outlines.

SIMPLE BATIK

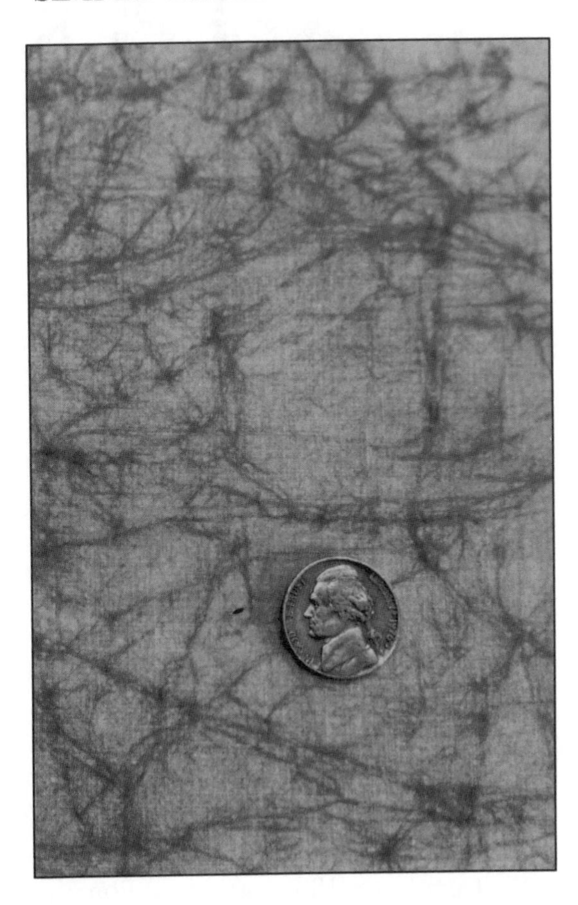

An overall delicate crackle pattern is produced by waxing the entire piece of fabric with 1 part by weight beeswax and 3 parts by weight paraffin.

The fabric may be waxed by dipping it into melted wax and stretching it flat to cool. Fabric may also be waxed in an electric skillet. Put the fabric in the skillet set at 250 degrees F. and rub over it with a block of wax until the wax penetrates. Remove the fabric and lay it flat to cool.

When the wax cools and hardens, crumple or twist the fabric into a tight ball to crack the wax. Dye the fabric. Fine veins and various shades of the dye color decorate the fabric. Follow Step 8 of the General Directions to remove the wax.

BEEKEEPERS' FORMULAS

BEE KILL

A spray made of 1 cup dishwashing liquid to 1 gallon water kills honeybees quickly and economically.

CANDY BOARDS

Candy boards can be used any time of year to provide food stores for honey-bees without stimulating brood rearing.

10 pounds granulated sugar
2 pounds corn syrup
2 2/3 cup water
1/4 teaspoon cream of tartar

While stirring, heat the ingredients to 242 degrees F. Remove the mixture from the heat and, with an electric mixer, beat it until it cools to 180 degrees F. Pour it into four 9-by-12-inch non-stick cookie pans and let it cool.

POLLEN SUBSTITUTE

Ounces by weight:
2 ounces pollen
5.5 ounces water
10.5 ounces powdered sugar
6 ounces soybean flour

The pollen must be from disease-free colonies. Mix the pollen, water and sugar. Add the soybean flour and stir until the mixture resembles peanut butter. Make pancake-size patties with waxed paper on each side. These can be stored in the freezer and later placed over the brood nest (under the inner cover). Each patty lasts 10 to 14 days in the hive.

PUBLICATIONS AVAILABLE

Dr. James Tew, Extension Service, United States Department of Agriculture has compiled a listing of state beekeeping publications that are available. The list of 260 publications is cross referenced in a table of contents. Addresses and prices are included. To receive a copy send $5.00 to: Ms. Sharon Ferrell, OSU Extension Bee Lab, OARDS/Department of Entomology, 1680 Madison Avenue, Wooster, OH 44691 USA.

STINGS

Papain is a protelytic enzyme extracted from the skins of papayas. It is sold by some beer-making and herb suppliers (see "Alternative Beverage," Appendix A). Papain neutralizes honeybee venom and relieves pain from the sting. Sprinkle an ice cube with papain and apply it to the sting site. Take the recommended dosage of an antihistamine.

WAX MOTHS

To prevent wax moth damage to stored combs, stack supers no more than 8 high. Seal any cracks with tape. Place 6 table-spoons of *paradichlorobenzene* (moth crystals) on an inner cover at the top of the stack and cover. The evaporation rate of the crystals depends on the temper-ature. Check them every 7 to 10 days and renew them as they evaporate. All moth crystals and moth balls are not paradichlorobenzene. **Note:** Supers of combs infested with wax moth larvae can be placed over fire ant dens. Be sure the den has not been treated with poison. Fire ants eat the larvae without damage to the combs.

BEER - HONEY ALE

As of 1979, federal law allows any adult to make 100 gallons of wine and beer per year for personal use. Households with two adults may make 200 gallons each year. It is illegal to sell beer without a license.

Zymurgy is a magazine for home brewers. It is included in membership to:

The American Homebrewer's Association
Post Office Box 1679
Boulder, Colorado 80306-1679

Recommended Reading
The New Complete Joy of Home Brewing
by Charlie Papazian

EQUIPMENT AND SUPPLIES

- ❏ 5-gallon glass carboy
- ❏ 6.7-gallon plastic fermentation bucket with cover and air lock
- ❏ 6 feet of 3/8-inch clear plastic hose
- ❏ 1 air lock (See page 55.)
- ❏ Carboy stopper drilled to fit the air lock
- ❏ Floating thermometer (32 to 212 degrees F.)
- ❏ Triple-scale hydrometer (.990 to 1.120 specific gravity)
- ❏ Bottles, caps and capper
- ❏ 3-to-4-gallon enamel or stainless steel pot
- ❏ Large funnel
- ❏ Long plastic stirrer

Request beer-making supply catalogs from "Alternative Beverage" and "Great Fermentations" (see Appendix A). Their advice lines can really be helpful to a beginner. The advice is free except for the price of the call.

"Alternative Beverage" 1-704-527-9643
"Great Fermentations" 1-415-459-2520

The catalog drawings and descriptions explain the equipment and ingredients. All equipment and supplies (even bottles) are sold by mail. The equipment used to make beer is the same as that used to make mead or wine (page 53). This formula makes five gallons. To make one gallon, divide the ingredients by five, except the yeast. One package of yeast is used for one to five gallons of beer.

HONEY ALE

One 3-to-4-pound can hopped malt extract
Approximately 3 to 4 pounds honey
1 package ale yeast
3/4 cup corn sugar (for bottling only)

GENERAL DIRECTIONS

Step 1: Sanitize everything that touches beer to kill airborne yeast and bacteria. Use a solution of 1 tablespoon chlorine laundry bleach to 1 gallon water. Soak the equipment for 15 minutes in the solution, then rinse it well in hot tap water. Save the solution as it may be used repeatedly (until the smell is gone). Never mix chlorine bleach with other cleaning agents.

Step 2: Combine the malt extract, 3 pounds honey and 1 1/2 gallons of water in a pot. Stir well and boil it over medium-high heat for 15 minutes. Watch the pot to be sure it doesn't boil over.

Step 3: Add 3 gallons of cold water to the sanitized fermentation bucket. Add the boiled ingredients to the water. Shake or stir the contents of the bucket to mix it well. Add enough water to equal 5 gallons. The mixture is called *wort* (pronounced "wert").

Step 4: When the wort is well mixed, add a floating thermometer and take a specific gravity reading with a sanitized hydrometer. A hydrometer is as easy to read as a thermometer and instructions come with it. Adjust the specific gravity between 1.043 and 1.048. To increase the specific gravity, add honey to the wort and stir well. To decrease the specific gravity, add water to the wort and stir well. When the specific gravity is accurate, adjust the wort volume to 5 gallons.

Step 5: Activate the yeast. To do this, take a cup of wort at 80 degrees F., sprinkle the ale yeast over it and wait until it foams (15 to 30 minutes). Wait until the wort in the bucket is between 70 and 75 degrees F. Add the yeast to the wort in the bucket and stir well.

Step 6: Divide the wort between the bucket and a carboy. Each should be only half full to allow for foaming. Attach sanitized air locks to the bucket and carboy. Add 3/4 inch water to both air locks. Place the wort in a dark place between 70 and 75 degrees F. Fermentation starts within 8 to 24 hours.

Step 7: After 3 or 4 days of fermentation, foaming will subside. Pour the wort into the carboy. Insert an air lock containing 3/4 inch water. Place the wort in a dark place to continue fermentation.

Step 8: When bubbles quit coming through the air lock (3 to 5 weeks, depending on the temperature), take a specific gravity reading. Bottle the beer if the reading is between 1.000 and 1.005. If the reading is higher, wait 2 to 3 days and take another reading. If the reading is unchanged, the beer is ready to bottle even if the reading is higher than 1.005.

Step 9: Prepare the priming solution. To do this, siphon 2 quarts of beer from the carboy into a pan. Add 3/4 cup corn sugar, boil the mixture 5 minutes, and let it cool. The sugar creates carbonation in the bottles. Never exceed the recommended amount of sugar and always use bottles that can withstand carbonation pressure.

Step 10: Pour the priming solution into a sanitized bucket. With as little splashing as possible, siphon the beer off the yeast deposit into the bucket. Stir it gently to mix it, but introduce as little oxygen as possible.

Step 11: Clean and sanitize the bottles, caps, and any other equipment that will touch the beer. Caps that fit beer bottles also fit domestic champagne bottles. Siphon the beer into bottles, leaving a 1-inch headspace. Cap the bottles and store them upright for 3 weeks at 70 degrees F. The beer will continue to clear and improve for several months.

Step 12: Chill the beer upright in a refrigerator. Each bottle contains a sediment of yeast. Open the bottle and pour all but the last 1/2 inch of beer into a glass.

ESTIMATING ALCOHOL

To estimate the alcohol content of beer, subtract the ending specific gravity from the beginning specific gravity and multiply by 150. This number represents the percentage of alcohol by weight.

Example:

Beginning gravity	1.045
Ending gravity	1.005
Difference	.040
Multiplied by	150
Alcohol	6.00%

CANDLES - DIPPED

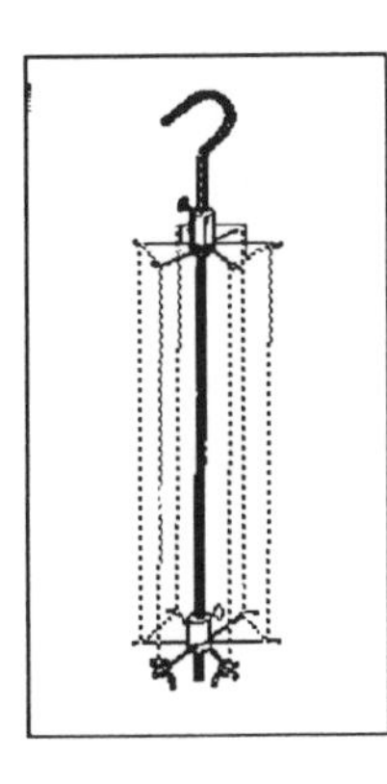

Candle-making suppliers sell frames to make dipped candles, but a few dipped candles can be made without special equipment. Molded candles are often dipped to achieve a smooth surface or to simulate the hand-dipped look.

GENERAL DIRECTIONS

Step 1: Choose a container for the wax that is tall and thin so that the entire length of the candle can be dipped. Use 24-ply flat-braid wicks for candles up to one-inch in diameter.

Step 2: Make a double boiler by placing the can in a pot and by placing wooden strips beneath the can to raise it an inch or so from the bottom.

Step 3: Add wax to the can and add water to the pot. Heat the wax until its temperature is between 155 and 165 degrees F. Place the wick in the wax and allow it to soak for about 5 minutes.

Step 4: Remove the wick, straighten it and tie a weight to one end. Dip the wick into the wax and immediately remove it in a smooth motion. The wick should be dipped to the top of the candle each time and allowed a minute to cool between dips. Continue the dipping process until the candle is a little larger than a pencil. Clip the wick at the base to remove the weight and to flatten the base of the candle. Continue dipping until the candle is the desired diameter. A 3/4-inch diameter candle will require about 25 dips.

Step 5: Cut the base of the candle flat and dip it one or two more times to finish it. A small drip of wax should remain on the base. This is attractive and a trademark of hand-dipped candles.

BALLOON SHELL

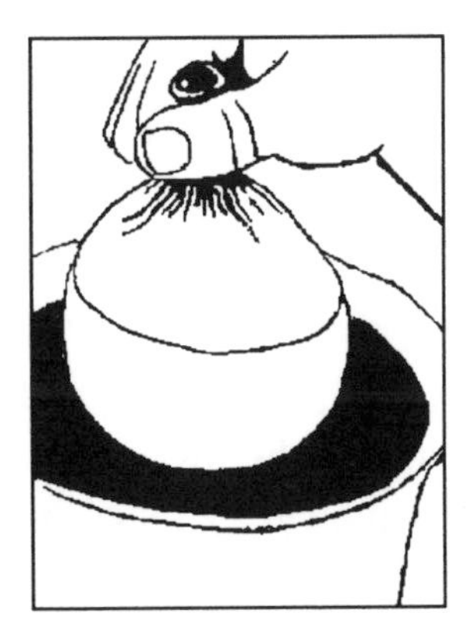

Fill a balloon with water to the size shell desired. Dip the balloon into 160-degree F. wax. Allow the wax to cool between each dip. Continue dipping until the shell is about 1/4-inch thick. Hang the balloon until the wax cools. Pop the balloon and remove it. Trim the top of the shell with a knife if necessary, or line an electric skillet in foil and smooth the top of the shell by rubbing it over the heated surface (200 degrees F.). Place a candle in the shell to make a floating candle, or wick the shell and fill it with wax to make a solid candle.

RICE PAPER

Rice paper disappears when dipped into melted wax. Write messages or designs on rice paper. When the candle is almost finished, apply the paper to the melted wax. Dip the candle again. The paper is barely noticeable and only the writing seems embedded. Look for rice paper where stationery is sold, or order patterned rice paper from "Deep Flex" (see Appendix A).

CANDLES - MOLDED

Molds: Follow the manufacturer's instructions when using their molds. If no wax temperature is suggested with the mold, pour beeswax at 160 degrees F. Beeswax is slightly tacky and sometimes difficult to remove from metal and plastic molds unless a wax-release agent is used. Flexible, rubber-type molds such as polyurethane are excellent for molding beeswax. Wash the mold in soapy water after each use and release agents will not be necessary. To make original molds, see pages 66-69.

Color: The natural color of beeswax proves that it is indeed beeswax. The quality of the wax is judged by its color. Good quality beeswax is straw to canary yellow in color. Brown or greenish tints indicate the presence of impurities. Pure white beeswax indicates that the wax has been chemically bleached. If artificial coloring is desired, use coloring designed for candles. Follow the manufacturer's directions. Colored crayons, lipstick and artist's oil paints all have disadvantages when used to color wax. The yellow of beeswax alters some colors added to it, especially light shades of blue and purple. The light yellow of beeswax plus light blue equals light green. To bleach beeswax, see page 103.

Scent: Add the amount of candle scent advised by the manufacturer or use 1/2 teaspoon essential oil for each pound of beeswax. See page 28 for essential oils.

WARNING: Never use candle scents in food, cosmetics or any product other than candles.

Pouring: Pouring wax into a mold too fast produces bubbles that can ruin the cast. Pouring wax too slowly produces lines along the casting. It is best to have the pouring spout close to the mold and pour into the center (or deepest part) of the mold. Do not pour wax down the sides.

Shrinkage: When beeswax is poured into a large mold and cooled, a crust often forms on top. Puncture that layer down into the melted wax. This opens the candle, eliminates air pockets and ensures more even burning. Fill the depression with more wax. Repeat the puncturing and filling until the candle is solid. Allow the candle to cool completely before removing it from the mold. The candle will become harder during the next 2 to 3 days.

Cracking: If beeswax is heated to a high temperature (over 180 degrees F) and poured into a large mold it could crack as it cools. Prevent cracking by placing the mold of wax in a preheated 200 degree F. oven. Turn off the oven and allow the wax to cool without opening the oven door.

Bloom: Over time, the surface of beeswax may become coated with a white, frosty coating called "bloom." Some people like the bloom of beeswax. If a glossy wax is desired, polish the wax with nylon or polyester cloth. To form a matte finish, wipe the wax with a cloth moistened with turpentine, mineral spirits or cigarette lighter fluid (naphtha). Allow the wax to dry without polishing it.

CANDLE APPLIQUÉ

See pages 15 and 64.

CANDLE FORMULA I

Candles of 100% beeswax burn longer, more cleanly and give off more light than other wax candles. Beeswax is symbolic of nature and of the beekeeping craft. Candles made of 100% beeswax with no artificial coloring or scent are the most elegant candles made.

CANDLE FORMULA II

1 pound beeswax
2 pounds tallow (Directions for rendering fat are on page 93.)
6 ounces (weight) stearic acid
2 tablespoons candle scent

This is an old-fashioned formula and the candle scent is definitely *not* optional.

CRAFT WAX SHELL

Wind sheets of craft wax to fit inside a candle mold. The craft wax shell should be at least 1/2 inch thick. Pour 160 degree F. beeswax into the shell. (See page 14 for craft wax rolled candles.)

ENGRAVING AND IMPRINTING

Candles can be imprinted with heated nails or tooled with an electric wood burning pen. This method is particularly striking when used on a beeswax candle that has been dipped into colored wax. Engraving reveals beeswax beneath the dipped layer of color.

HERB CANDLES

Dried herbs can be stirred into melted beeswax and left to become part of the finished candle. The leaves in the following formula distribute evenly throughout the candle. If other herbs are used, be aware that some float and others sink to the bottom.

Ounces by weight:
8 ounces beeswax
4 ounces 143/145 paraffin wax
1 ounce dried lemon verbena or rosemary leaves (no stems)

Melt the wax to 160 degrees F. and stir in the dried herbs. Pour the wax into molds.

MOLDS, MAKING

See pages 66-69.

STICKY WAX

Small pieces of this wax are used to hold candles in their holders or to attach wax appliqué to candles. "Sticky Wax" can be used to attach pieces of carving wax (see page 16) and modeling wax (see page 64).

4 ounces (weight) beeswax
2 tablespoons turpentine or mineral spirits

Melt the beeswax in a microwave or double boiler. Remove it from the heat and stir in the turpentine. When the mixture cools, knead the wax to soften it. Pull, roll, pinch and twist this wax into shapes. Store it in an air-tight container.

PAINTING WAX

Beeswax can be painted with acrylic paint, candle coloring, artist's oil paints or "Encaustic Wax" (see page 25). Oil paint takes days, sometimes weeks, to dry.

SAND SHELL

1 part by weight beeswax
2 parts by weight sand

Melt the wax to 180 degrees F. and stir in the sand. Use a knife or spatula to apply a layer of the mixture evenly to the sides and base of a mold. Let this cool and harden. When the mixture is firm, embed a wick in it and secure the wick at the top. Fill the shell with wax. Dip the finished candle in melted beeswax. If desired, carve patterns out of the sand layer so that the inner wax core shows through.

SAND MOLDS

See page 68.

WHIPPED WAX

Apply whipped wax to surfaces to give them the appearance of snow, frosting or whipped cream.

1 pound beeswax
1 tablespoon cornstarch
1 tablespoon dishwashing liquid

Melt the beeswax in a microwave or a double boiler. Combine the cornstarch and dishwashing liquid. Remove the wax from heat, combine the ingredients, and wait until a surface film appears on the mixture. Use a beater to whip the wax until it is the consistency of cake frosting. While it is still warm, quickly apply the whipped wax to a candle or other surface. If the wax cools too much to be spread with a spatula, repeat the heating and beating process.

CANDLES - ROLLED

Beeswax foundation is cream colored and embossed with bee cells. It is always 100% beeswax. Craft wax is embossed with bee cells, available in many colors and it sometimes contains paraffin. Beeswax foundation and craft wax are sold by beekeeping and candle-making suppliers (see Appendix A). "Modeling Wax" (see page 64) can be formed into sheets and used to make rolled candles.

WICKS

Choosing the proper wick for a rolled candle is an art. A rolled candle contains less wax than a poured candle of the same diameter. Charts listing wick sizes for poured candles are not accurate for rolled candles.

♦ For candles made from 1/2 sheet of craft wax, use 18-ply, flat-braid wicking.

♦ Use 24-ply, flat-braid or W-59/30 square wick in rolled candles up to 2 inches in diameter.

Increase the wick size in proportion to the diameter of the candle. Leave 1/4 inch wick at both ends of the candle. After burning one end, turn the candle over for a new wick.

ROLLING

Beeswax foundation and craft wax should be 80 degrees F. to roll properly. Lay the wick on the wax and crimp the edge of the wax over the wick. Roll the sheet tightly and evenly.

One candle from one sheet
1 2/3 inch diameter by 8 inch height

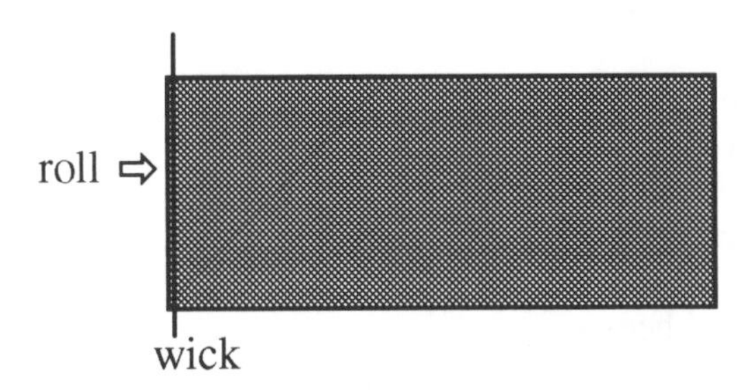

Two tapers from one sheet
3/4 inch diameter by 8 inch height

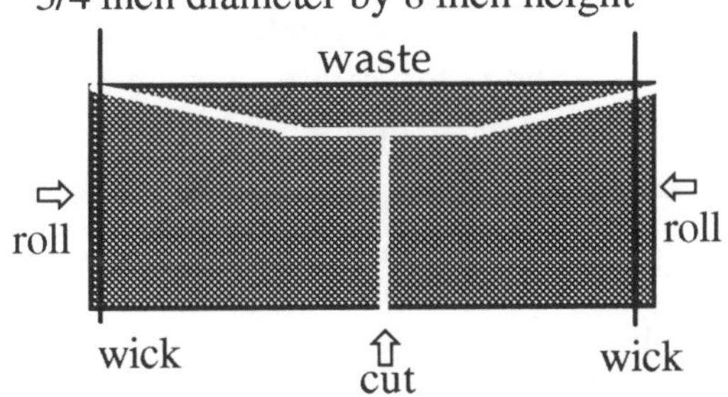

Make appliqué for candles by cutting sheets craft wax. If the wax is warm enough, no adhesive is necessary. Simply press the appliqué onto the candle. Three-dimensional bows and flowers can also be made from craft wax. (See page 64 for "Modeling Wax Appliqué".)

Two Christmas trees from five sheets
4 1/2-inch base by 8-inch height

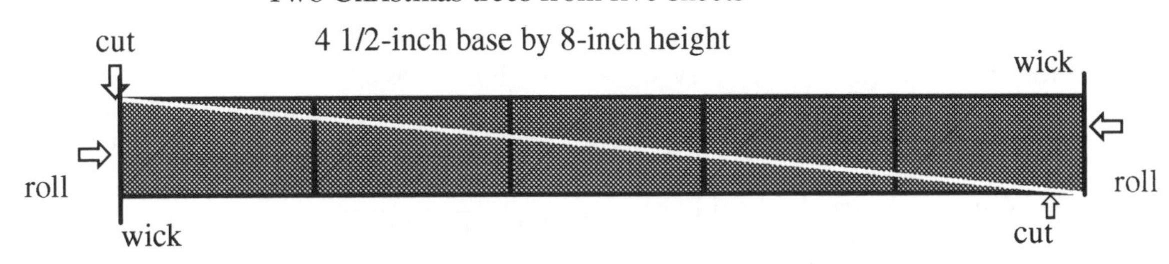

Notes and Clippings

CARVING WAX

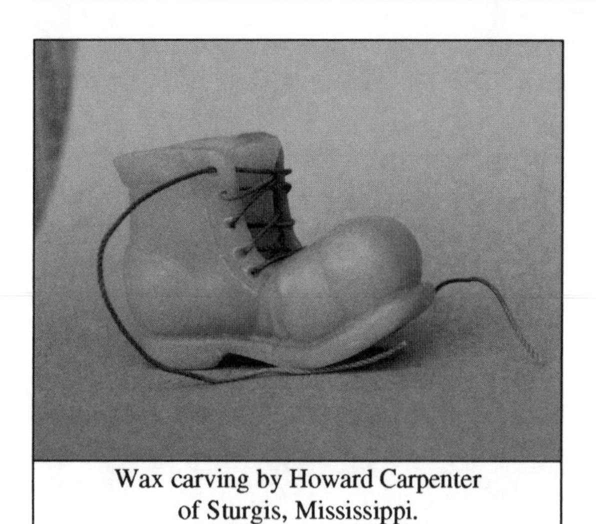

Wax carving by Howard Carpenter
of Sturgis, Mississippi.

Beeswax is usually combined with other substances to make it more suitable for carving. A hard wax is preferable, but not one so brittle as to flake off or chip while being carved. The ingredients are listed as parts by weight. Use ounces or pounds, depending on the size blank required for the carving. Objects carved from wax can be cast in metal. See page 49 for "Lost Wax Investment Casting".

"Intricate Carving Waxes" should be carved with very thin blades or dental tools. These waxes are good for small intricate carvings such as models for jewelry. "Wax for Knife Carving" is suitable for carving with a thick blade such as a pocket knife.

INTRICATE CARVING WAX I

5 parts beeswax wax
5 parts carnauba wax
1 part stearic acid

INTRICATE CARVING WAX II

10 parts beeswax
10 parts carnauba wax
1 part alum

WAX FOR KNIFE CARVINGS

1 pound beeswax
1/2 cup cornstarch or talcum powder

GENERAL DIRECTIONS

Ingredients are sold by candle-making suppliers. Carving tools are available from "Woodworker's Supply" and "Earth Guild" (see Appendix A). Check the library for books about wood carving. Many of them contain patterns that are easy to follow.

Step 1: Melt the waxes in a 200 degree F. oven. Add powdered additives (if any) and candle coloring, if desired. Wait until the wax cools to 160 degrees F. and pour it into a mold. The size mold depends on the size carving desired. Paper milk cartons are available in many sizes and serve well as molds. Carving wax can also be poured into shallow molds (1-to-3-inches thick) and used for relief carvings.

Step 2: When the wax is cool, remove it from the mold. If wax cartons were used as molds, tear off the paper to release the wax. Let the wax harden for 2 or 3 days before carving it.

Step 3: Carve the wax. Save pieces of wax carved from the blank. They can be added to the wax when the next blank is made. Wax builds up on the knife; clean it often on a cloth moistened with turpentine or mineral spirits.

CHRISTMAS ORNAMENTS

The idea of wax Christmas tree ornaments is not new. Before blown-glass ornaments were popular, colonial women molded Christmas tree ornaments from beeswax. At one time wax ornaments imported from Germany were an important part of our Christmas tradition. Order beeswax and molds from candle-making suppliers. "Pourette" and "Deep Flex" (see Appendix A) carry an extensive line of Christmas appliqué molds. Antique candy and cookie molds make interesting forms.

GENERAL DIRECTIONS

Step 1: Melt the wax to 165 degrees F. Cut a 6-inch length of gold cord or ribbon. Make a loop by gluing the ends together or by dipping 1/2 inch of both ends into melted wax. Hold the ends together until the wax cools.

Step 2: Pour wax into the mold and wait until about 1/8-inch of the outside is cool and opaque, but the center is still hot, liquid and translucent. Insert the joined ends into the wax, leaving the loop extending out of the mold.

Step 3: When the wax is cool, remove the ornament from the mold. Note that wax ornaments should not be stored in a hot attic. Beeswax melts near 146 degrees F., but thin ornaments can warp at a much lower temperature.

COLOR CHART

This chart is helpful when mixing colors or when dyeing one color over another. To be sure that the chart is read correctly, find the following: ♦ Red over red produces darker red. ♦ Orange over brown produces tobacco brown. ♦ Brown over blue produces almost black.

	Over Red Produces	Over Blue Produces	Over Yellow Produces	Over Brown Produces	Over Orange Produces	Over Green Produces	Over Purple Produces
Red	Darker Red	Purple	Scarlet	Reddish Brown	Light Red	Dull Brown	Reddish Purple
Blue	Purple	Deep Blue	Green	Very Dark Brown	Dull Dark Gray	Bottle Green	Bluish Purple
Yellow	Scarlet	Green	Deep Yellow	Golden Brown	Yellow Orange	Light Green	Greenish Brown
Brown	Brownish Red	Almost Black	Yellowish Brown	Darker Brown	Yellowish Dark Brown	Dull Greenish Brown	Chocolate
Orange	Light Red	Dull Dark Gray	Light Orange	Tobacco Brown	Deep Orange	Yellowish Green	Reddish Brown
Green	Almost Black	Greenish Blue	Light Green	Olive Green	Myrtle Green	Darker Green	Dull Dark Green
Purple	Reddish Purple	Plum	Almost Black	Very Dark Reddish Brown	Light Dull Purple	Dull Dark Purple	Darker Purple

CREAMED HONEY

A canned cake (also see page 33) and creamed honey.

The following are terms for honey intentionally granulated with crystals as small (fine) as possible:

Candied honey
Creamed honey
Crystallized honey
Granulated honey
Honey creme
Honey fondant
Honey spread
Spun honey
Whipped honey

Although it is still 100% honey, some say the flavor of honey is improved by creaming. At room temperature (70 to 80 degrees F.), creamed honey does not drip and is easily spread with a knife. If a softer product is desired, it can be kept in a warmer place, but above 80 degrees F. it will begin to liquefy. Even if liquefied creamed honey is returned to a cooler place, it will not return to its former state. For creaming, honey with a moisture content of 17.5% to 18% is ideal.

Given time, honey will granulate or crystallize. Crystallized honey is vulnerable to fermentation due to the increased moisture content of the honey not yet crystallized. Naturally crystallized honey is undesirable for its large crystals that cause a coarse texture. Coarsely crystallized honey can be liquefied in hot water, or it can be run through a food processor to break up the crystals and to obtain a smoother texture.

GENERAL DIRECTIONS

2 pounds creamed honey
10 pounds liquid honey

Creamed honey is sold in stores next to the liquid honey. Use freshly extracted, strained honey that is at room temperature. Mix the liquid honey and creamed honey for 15 minutes. Incorporate as little air as possible. Set the honey aside for 1 day. Remove any foam that comes to the surface. Store the honey in small containers between 45 and 57 degrees F. See page 94 for temperature control. Granulation should be complete within 1 to 3 weeks.

♦ Fruit Flavors

Concentrated flavoring such as extracts and fruit syrups can be used to flavor creamed honey.

♦ Cinnamon

Mix 3 tablespoons ground cinnamon with 1 pound creamed honey.

♦ Nut or Fruit Creamed Honey

Mix 1 measure creamed honey with 1 measure nuts, coconut or chopped dried fruits.

CURIOSITIES

These formulas are taken from very old sources exactly as they were written. As they are for entertainment purposes only, no suppliers of ingredients or detailed instructions are provided.

ANGOSTURA BITTERS

4 ounces gentian root
10 ounces calisaya bark
10 ounces Canada snake root
10 ounces Virginia snake root
10 ounces liquorice root
10 ounces yellow bark
10 ounces allspice
10 ounces dandelion root
10 ounces Angostura bark
6 ounces cardamom seeds
4 ounces balsam of tolu
4 ounces orangetis
4 ounces Turkey rhubarb
4 ounces galanga
1 pound orange peel
1 pound alkanet root
1 1/2 ounces caraway seed
1 1/2 ounces cinnamon
1/2 ounce cloves
2 ounces nutmeg
2 ounces coriander seed
2 ounces catechu
2 ounces wormwood
1 ounce mace
1 1/4 pounds red saunders
8 ounces curcuma
30 pounds honey

Pound the ingredients to a coarse powder and steep for 15 days in 50 gallons proof spirit, stirring occasionally. Then rack it off and mix the honey and sufficient caramel to make it a dark red. Let the whole settle, then filter.

EMBALMING PREPARATION

This formula is both a wound filler and a modeling wax for making noses, ears, etc., in reconstruction of accident cases.

Parts by weight:
10 parts paraffin wax
10 parts petroleum jelly
5 parts beeswax
2 parts soap flakes
5 parts water

Melt the waxes and petroleum jelly to 160 degrees F. Separately, heat the soap and water to 160 degrees F. Combine the two mixtures. Stir and color to suit. As a wound filler, use the formula as it is. For modeling, add up to 8 parts starch.

GOLD INK

The best gold ink is made by rubbing up gold leaf as thoroughly as possible with a little honey. The honey is then washed away with water, and the finely powdered gold leaf left is mixed to the consistency of a writing ink with weak gum water. Everything depends upon the fineness of the gold powder, i.e., upon the diligence with which it has been worked with the honey. Precipitated gold is finer than can be got by any rubbing, but its color is wrong, being dark brown. The above gold ink should be used with a quill pen.

GILDERS' WAX

For the production of various colorings of gold in fire gilding, the respective places are frequently covered with gilders' wax. These consist of various chemicals which have an etching action in red heat upon the bronze mass, the etching causing roughness of unequal depth and the color being affected in consequence. The gilding wax is prepared by melting together the finely powdered chemicals with wax according to the following.

Formula Number	I	II	III	IV	V
Beeswax	32	32	32	96	36
Red chalk	3	24	18	48	18
Verdigris	2	4	18	32	18
Burnt alum	2	4	0	0	0
Burnt borax	0	0	2	1	3
Copper ash	0	4	5	20	8
Zinc vitriol	0	0	0	32	18
Green vitriol	0	0	0	1	6

HARNESS WAX

Parts by weight:
90 parts oil of turpentine
9 parts beeswax
1 part Prussian blue
0.5 parts indigo
5 parts bone black

Melt the wax in the oil by the aid of low heat on a water bath. Mix in the remaining ingredients.

HONEY WATER

Toilet waters proper are perfumed liquids designed more specially as refreshing applications to the person, accessories to the bath and to the operation of the barber. They should not be of so persistent a character as the "extracts" commonly used for that purpose, as they would then be unsuitable as lotions.

1 pound best honey
1 pound coriander seed
1 1/2 ounces cloves
1 ounce nutmegs
1 ounce gum benjamin
1 drachm vanilloes, Number 4
3 lemon rinds

Bruise the cloves, nutmegs, coriander seed and benjamin. Cut the vanilloes in pieces and put all into a glass alembic with 1 gallon of clean rectified spirit. After digesting 48 hours, draw off the spirit by distillation. To 1 gallon of the distilled spirit add:

1 1/2 pounds damask rose water
1 1/2 pounds orange flower water
5 grains musk
5 grains ambergris

Grind the musk and ambergris in a glass mortar and put all together into a digesting vessel. Let circulate 3 days and nights in a gentle heat; then let cool. Filter and keep the water in well-stoppered bottles.

SUPPOSITORY BASE

Suppositories melt at body temperature.

Parts by weight:
1.5 parts beeswax
4.5 parts cocoa butter
4.0 parts cod liver oil

Melt the ingredients in a microwave or a small can placed in boiling water. Pour the mixture into molds. Store suppositories in the refrigerator.

TOOTHPASTE

Parts by weight:
250 parts honey
250 parts precipitated chalk
250 parts orris root
7 parts tincture of opium
7 parts tincture of myrrh
2 parts oil of rose
2 parts oil of cloves
2 parts oil of nutmeg

Mix all ingredients well.

DAIRY PRODUCTS

CHEESE WAX

After the air-drying period, when cheese has developed a hard, dry rind, it must be protected with wax to prevent mold and further drying. (See page 99 to prevent mold on unwaxed cheese.)

Ounces by weight:
13.5 ounces beeswax
2.5 ounces vegetable shortening

Heat the ingredients in an oven at 200 degrees F. until combined. Remove the wax from the oven and wait for it to reach 160 to 180 degrees F. Dip the cheese and remove it with one quick, smooth motion. Repeat this step until the wax is about 1/16th-inch thick.

KUMISS

Kumiss is a refreshing and nutritious dairy drink. Because kumiss is slightly carbonated, it has been called "the Russian champagne of dairy products." This formula produces a rich creamy drink with bubbly effervescence.

1 gallon skim milk
2 tablespoons honey
1/8 teaspoon champagne yeast

Step 1: Heat the milk to 180 degrees F. Add the honey, mix well and cool to 70 degrees F.
Step 2: Dissolve the yeast in 1/4 cup warm water (115 degree F. for 3 minutes) and stir it into the milk mixture.
Step 3: Cover the mixture with a clean cloth and allow it to stand at room temperature for 24 hours.
Step 4: Bottle kumiss in sanitized beer, soft drink or champagne bottles that withstand carbonation pressure. Crown caps for soft drinks also fit beer and domestic champagne bottles. Buy crown caps and a hammer capper to apply the caps from wine-making suppliers. Plastic soda bottles up to the 2-liter size can be reused if the caps fit tightly.
Step 5: Store the bottled kumiss at room temperature for 24 hours, then place it in a refrigerator. Shake the bottles every few days, but not just before opening them. Kumiss will keep for 6 to 8 weeks and becomes increasingly acid. If the degree of acidity is objectionable, it can be masked by adding honey.

SWEET CHEESE

Sweet cheese is a Hungarian food, traditionally served at Easter. It is an appetizing hors d'oeuvre or a wholesome snack.

1 1/2 quarts milk
12 eggs
4 tablespoons honey
1 teaspoon salt
1/4 teaspoon nutmeg

Beat the eggs, honey, salt and nutmeg until well blended. Heat the milk to a boil while stirring constantly. Add the egg mixture and boil for 5 minutes or until the mixture curdles. Remove it from the heat; if desired, stir in 1 1/2 cup raisins and 1 cup broken pecans. Line a colander with a clean dishcloth or cheesecloth. Pour the curdled milk into the colander. Put on rubber gloves as protection from the hot liquid. Pull the corners of the cloth together and twist tightly to squeeze out as much liquid as possible and to form the solids into a ball. Hang the cheese to drain 3 to 4 hours or until it is cold. The cheese is ready to eat now or it can be stored in a refrigerator.

DOLLS OF WAX

"Megan," a wax doll by the author.

The following method of making a wax doll is a little unorthodox, but no sculpting is required, it's inexpensive and it teaches everything one needs to know to create an original wax doll.

Wax dolls are sometimes carved or sculpted from wax. It is more common for the head, arms and legs to be molded in wax and attached to a stuffed cloth body.

Doll-making suppliers (see Appendix A) sell expensive molds designed for porcelain that can be used for molding wax. The manufacturers usually recommend the size of the wig and eyes that will fit a porcelain doll cast in the mold. Wax has very little shrinkage. Wax dolls cast in molds for porcelain require a full size larger eyes and wig.

Most dollmakers sculpt the doll in clay, bake the clay to harden it, and make a mold from the sculpture. Talent and an eye for proportion are a must for someone who wishes to sculpt the model. "Super Sculpty", sold by craft stores, is an excellent clay for this type sculpting. It becomes hard when baked at 275 degrees F. for 15 minutes. It can then be sanded and carved or have more clay added and baked again.

Recommended Reading

Modern Wax Doll Art
by Carol Carlton
Available from Barker Enterprises
(See Appendix A for the address)
and
Making Beautiful Wax Dolls
by Judy Meier
Available from Scott Publications
30595 West 8 Mile Road
Livonia, Michigan 48152
1-313-477-6650

Doll Crafter magazine is also available from Scott Publications.

The International Dollmakers Association is designed to unite dollmakers and to promote the art of dollmaking.

The International Dollmakers
Association
6408 Glendale Street
Metairie, Louisiana 70003

EQUIPMENT AND SUPPLIES

- ❑ Acrylic paint
- ❑ A cloth-bodied doll with a wig
- ❑ Liquid rubber latex or plaster of Paris
- ❑ Formula ingredients

The equipment and supplies are sold by candle-making suppliers, craft stores and doll-making suppliers. Before ordering anything by mail, check the craft section of the local discount department store. A cloth-bodied doll with plastic arms, legs and head costs less than $10.00.

WAX DOLL FORMULA

1 cup household paraffin
1/4 cup cornstarch
1 cup beeswax (light yellow to white)
2 tablespoons stearic acid
1/4 cup talcum powder
Red and brown candle coloring

GENERAL DIRECTIONS

Step 1: Remove the wig. It is probably glued on with rubber cement. Begin at the back edge and pull forcefully. It should come off without damage.

Step 2: Cut the thread or plastic holding the cloth body onto the neck. Split the stitches of the back seam all the way down.

Step 3: Pull the stuffing out of the body. Push an arm into the fabric, turning it wrong side out. Remove the string that holds the cuff onto the arm. Repeat this for the other arm and two legs.

Step 4: When the doll is completely disassembled, draw a pattern of each piece. The pattern and measurements can be used later to make an original wax doll.

Step 5: See page 67 for "Molds: Liquid Latex Rubber". Follow the instructions and make molds from the arms and legs.

Step 6:
FOR WAX DOLLS WITH PAINTED EYES
(Optional directions for Wax Dolls with Glass Eyes are given at the end of this section.)
A rubber mold cannot be pulled over the heads of most dolls because of the small necks. Wrap "Modeling Wax" (see the Index) around the neck as shown. This makes the neck larger so that the mold can be pulled off over the head. Brush liquid rubber latex over the model and wax to make a mold.

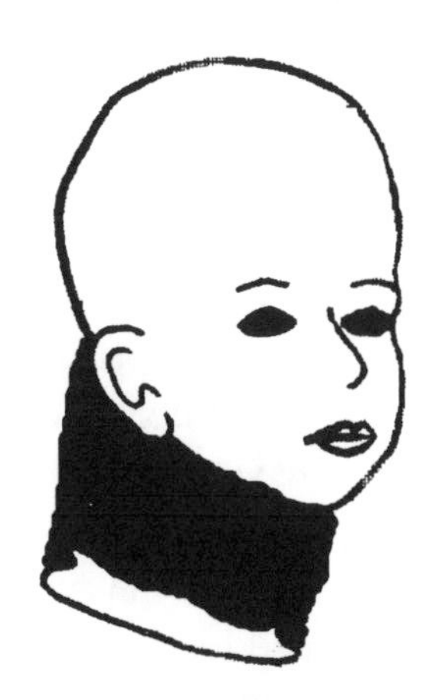

Step 7: Prepare the wax formula. Melt the waxes to 170 degrees F. If light yellow beeswax is used, only a small amount of red coloring may be necessary. If white beeswax is used, color it with a small shaving of red and an equal amount of brown. Test the color by dropping a spoonful of wax into cold water.

Step 8: The dry ingredients have a tendency to settle to the bottom of melted wax. Stir the wax before pouring it into each mold. Pour the wax into the molds, wait for it to cool and remove it.

Step 9: Use the original doll head as a guide and carve away the excess wax at the neck. Imperfections can be polished away with a nylon cloth dampened with naphtha. Naphtha is often sold as cigarette lighter fluid. It can be used to dissolve oil, tar, wax, gum, labels, crayon and heel marks.

Step 10: Use the original as a guide and paint the wax doll's eyes, brows and lips with acrylic paint. Wait for the paint to dry. Use a finger to apply a small amount of lipstick over the cheek area. Rub the area to blend it. Dots of clear nail polish can be applied to the center of the lips and the eyes to create gloss.

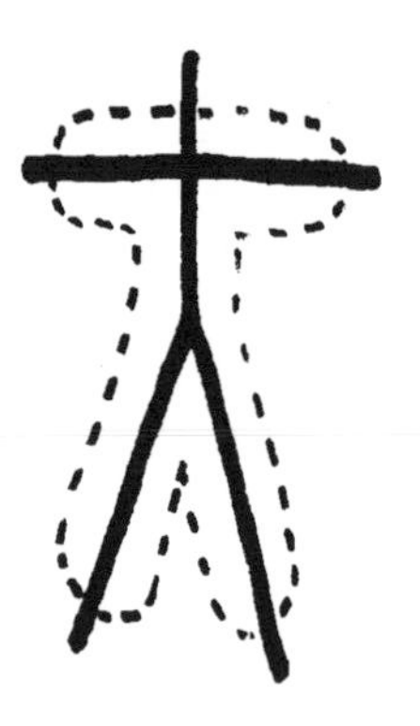

Step 11: Some inexpensive cloth bodied dolls have a wire running from arm to arm. Wax dolls should have a complete wire frame to allow the arms and legs to bend and to support the head. Use the pattern measurements and bend a coat hanger or similar strength wire to make a "stick man" frame. The frame should be about one inch longer than the cloth body at the neck, arm and leg openings. Reassemble the doll, using the wax parts instead of the original ones. Attach the arms and legs to the cloth body with string. Heat the wire frame to melt it into the arms and legs. Sew the back of the cloth body. Replace the stuffing with the aid of the eraser end of a pencil. Heat the wire frame and attach the head. Sew the neck closed. Glue on the wig with rubber cement.

OPTION FOR GLASS EYES IN A WAX SHELL HEAD

Step 1: Follow the General Directions until Step 6. See page 66 for "Molds: Plaster of Paris". Make a two-part mold of the head. The dividing line should be just behind the ears.

Step 2: Make a shell of the head by pouring melted wax into the mold. When 1/8-to-1/4-inch of the wax has cooled, pour the melted wax from the center of the head back into the wax pot. Wait for the shell to cool.

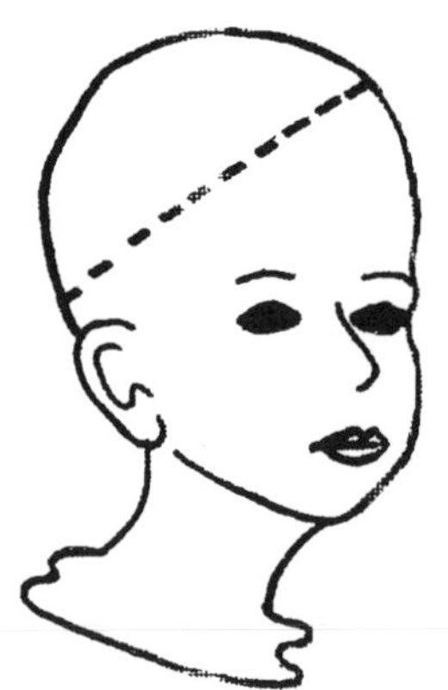

Step 3: Heat a knife in boiling water. Cut off the top of the wax head as shown. Use a small, thin-bladed knife to cut out the eye area. From inside the head, place the glass eyes. When the eyes are in position, drip wax from a burning candle onto them to hold them in place.

Step 4: Replace the piece that was cut from the head. Heat a knife or other metal instrument and melt the seam together. Wait for the wax to cool.

Step 5: Reinforce the head shell with plaster of Paris. Mix the plaster as the package directs. Half fill the head with plaster and roll the head so that plaster covers all sides. After about three rolls, pour out the excess plaster and set the head aside for the plaster to harden. Fill the head with 160 degree F. melted wax. Continue at Step 7 of the General Directions to complete the doll.

OPTION FOR GLASS EYES IN A SOLID WAX HEAD

Follow the General Directions until Step 9. Heat a metal tool over an alcohol burner and cut the eye sockets deep enough to contain the glass eyes. Melt the wax and use it to fill in around the eyes. Use a knife to carve away imperfections and a cloth dampened with naphtha to smooth the wax. Continue at Step 10 of the General Directions to complete the doll.

ENCAUSTIC PAINTING

The word, *encaustic* is derived from a Greek term meaning "burned-in." This method of painting with molten wax was used on most of the beautiful white marble statues now seen in museums. Realistic mummy portraits painted in the 4th century AD and an encaustic icon of the Madonna from 7th century Rome still exist.

The Encaustic Network Unlimited is an organization of established and beginning encaustic artists. They publish a quarterly newsletter.

Encaustic Network Unlimited
Post Office Box 8304
Federal Way, Washington 98003

EQUIPMENT AND SUPPLIES

Artist supply stores such as "Daniel Smith" and "Woodworker's Supply" sell many of the supplies. "Candlewic" and "Daniel Smith" sell an electric wax palette designed specifically for encaustic painting. See Appendix A for suppliers.

- ❑ Heat lamp
- ❑ Small cans and jars
- ❑ One brush for each color
- ❑ Electric buffer (optional)
- ❑ Propane torch (optional)
- ❑ Electric skillet or wax palette
- ❑ Beeswax
- ❑ Acrylic gesso
- ❑ Damar liquid varnish (5-pound cut)
- ❑ Artist canvas or 1/8-inch thick, untempered masonite panel
- ❑ Dry artist's pigments, fresco colors or artist's oil paint in tubes

WARNING: Some pigments are toxic. Avoid breathing the pigment dust and skin contact with it.

GENERAL DIRECTIONS

Step 1: Prepare a small panel to test the wax colors and a larger panel for the painting. Paint the canvas or the smooth side of the masonite panel with gesso. Apply the gesso by brushing in one direction. Allow it to dry and sand lightly to smooth it. Apply a second coat by brushing in the opposite direction. Allow it to dry and sand again.

Step 2: Line an electric skillet or griddle with aluminum foil to protect it. Set the temperature control at 300 degrees F. Put 1 pound of beeswax in a 1-pound coffee can and place this on the skillet. When the beeswax is melted (about 45 minutes), add to the skillet one small can for each color pigment.

Step 3: Prepare the medium formula.

ENCAUSTIC MEDIUM I

1 measure beeswax
3 measures turpentine
2 measures Canada balsam

Melt the beeswax in a microwave or a double boiler. Remove it from the heat and stir in the turpentine. Add dry pigments or oil paint from tubes to color the medium. Canada balsam is sold by "Chem Lab" (see Appendix A).

ENCAUSTIC MEDIUM II

4 measures beeswax
1 measure Damar varnish

Melt the beeswax and stir in the Damar varnish. Add dry pigments to color the medium.

ENCAUSTIC MEDIUM III

1 measure carnauba wax
3 measures beeswax

Melt the waxes and add dry pigments to color the medium.

When thinned with 15 measures of turpentine and not colored, this formula is a good wax for the final polish.

DRY PIGMENT TO MEDIUM

Some dry pigments are more concentrated than others. The table is a good estimate of dry pigment for each unit of medium. The left-hand column names the pigment. The middle column lists in volume measurements the ratio of pigment to medium: for one volume of medium, use the table volume of pigment. The right-hand column lists in weight measurements the ratio of pigment to medium: for one weight unit of medium, use the table weight unit of pigment.

Dry pigment	Pigment volume	Pigment weight
Alizarin crimson	2.3	0.66
Burnt sienna	2.2	1.66
Burnt umber	1.9	1.33
Cadmium orange	3.5	3.0
Cadmium red	3.0	3.0
Cadmium yellow	3.5	3.0
Cerulean blue	2.0	2.5
Chromium oxide green	2.0	3.4
Cobalt blue	1.0	1.66
Green earth	1.2	1.0
Indian red	4.0	3.66
Ivory black	1.1	1.0
Mars yellow	3.4	1.6
Naples yellow	2.0	4.0
Phthalocyanine blue	1.0	0.4
Phthalocyanine green	0.9	0.64
Prussian blue	2.8	1.14
Raw sienna	2.0	1.77
Raw umber	1.8	1.28
Titanium dioxide	1.8	2.0
Ultramarine blue	3.5	2.3
Venetian red	2.2	1.78
Viridian	1.8	1.11
White lead	6.0	7.5
Yellow ochre	3.0	2.0
Zinc oxide	5.4	5.0

Test each color on the small panel. The colors should be solid like oil paints on canvas. Add more pigment if necessary or thin the colors with turpentine if they are too thick.

Mix wax colors on the panel to form new colors. Write names or numbers beneath the colors if necessary to remember the combinations. Oil painting instruction books provide information about mixing colors to form new colors.

Step 4: Lower the skillet temperature to 250 degrees F. Smoothly spread a wax undercoat over the entire surface of the panel and create! Abstract painting allows for experimentation and is a good choice for the first project. Brush colors in various ways: short strokes, wavy lines, flicked on with the brush, poured from the cans and dropped on. Work quickly and do not try to blend the colors. The more colors added, spaced and over-lapped, the more unusual the abstract will be. Combining light, medium and dark colors also creates contrast. Observe the effects and get to know the medium. Clean the brushes in turpentine or lacquer thinner.

Step 5: Wait for the medium to dry and harden. Plug in a heat lamp and hold it in the center of the panel, 3 to 4 inches from the surface. Watch closely and move the lamp when the wax begins to soften and flow. Certain colors, such as white, melt more slowly than others. Various designs and patterns form. Continue moving the lamp and blending designs. All areas do not have to be blended.

Introduce texture while heating the painting by tipping the panel in various directions. The wax colors run and blend forming ridges, rivulets and layers. If colors disappear during the heating process, simply add more wax medium.

Step 6: Wait a day or two for the medium to harden. Polish it lightly with a soft cloth until the surface becomes shiny. Colors will brighten, obtain jewel tones and gain a three-dimensional look. The next day polish the painting with an electric buffer. When encaustic paintings are first completed the wax is soft and will cloud over. Polish them frequently during the first month. The surface will harden to look like an enameled surface. Frequent polishing will no longer be necessary.

ADVANCED BLENDING

An optional blending technique is done with a propane torch. Propane torches are sold by hardware stores. Read directions that come with the torch and be aware of fire hazards. Use a small, steady flame to create blow-out effects in the wax colors. White and other light colors are particularly effective when blown with a torch. Direct flame can ignite the medium. If so, remove the torch and with a breath of air, blow out the flame.

RELIEF ENCAUSTIC

This process combines encaustic techniques with relief carving in plaster. Carving tools are sold by "Woodworker's Supply" and "Earth Guild" (see Appendix A).

Plaster Base

5 measures plaster of Paris
2 measures water

Step 1: While stirring the water, sprinkle the plaster into it. Try not to splash or cause bubbles.

Step 2: Pour half the plaster into a shadow-box form that has a masonite back. Place metal mesh into the plaster to reinforce it. For hanging purposes, wires can be left standing free.

Step 3: Pour the remaining plaster. Carve the plaster while it is soft (which will be for many days). Allow the plaster to dry completely.

Step 4: Paint the plaster carving and blend the colors as directed in Step 5 of the General Directions.

Encaustic Medium for Plaster

This medium is thin enough to apply with a brush.

2 measures beeswax
4 measures Damar varnish
1 measure turpentine

Combine ingredients as described in the General Directions. This medium can be mixed with artist's oil paint from tubes and thinned with turpentine as desired.

ESSENTIAL OILS

Essential oils are highly concentrated extracts from natural plant materials such as fruits, flowers and spices. They contain no synthetic ingredients. One to ten pounds of plant material is used to make one ounce of oil. One ounce of oil contains approximately 360 drops. For example, one ounce of peppermint oil is approximately equivalent to 75 gallons of strong peppermint tea. Food-grade essential oils are designated as such, but all essential oils can be used to scent potpourri, candles, perfume, soap, and cosmetics. Consider aromatic and therapeutic traits of oils when choosing them to scent the formulas in this book. Store oils, tightly closed in a cool dark place, such as a refrigerator.

ANTISEPTIC VALUE

Experiments were conducted with *Staphylococcus pyogenes aureus* and *Streptococcus pyogenes* (common causes of boils and abscesses) and *Penicillium glaucum* and *Aspergillus albus* (two common molds). Based on these tests, essential oils may be classified as follows:

♦ **Highest antiseptic value**
Clove, wintergreen, sassafras, sandalwood, mint, thyme, cinnamon, camphor.

♦ **Good antiseptic value**
Eucalyptus, sage, lavender, violet.

♦ **Fair antiseptic value**
Juniper, rose, bergamot, patchouli, vanilla, verbena.

♦ **Low antiseptic value**
Neroli, geranium, jasmine, lemon-grass.

AROMA THERAPY

Aroma therapy has been practiced since ancient times and is one of the fastest-growing modes of alternative medicine. The few scientific studies that have been done on aroma therapy reinforce the therapeutic value of essential oils. Researchers at Milan University have successfully treated depression and anxiety using aerosol oils.

Inhaled through the nose, essential oils stimulate olfactory organs, which are linked to the areas of the brain that control emotions. Different oils elicit different physical and emotional responses.

Never inhale essential oils directly from the bottle. Mix 2 drops of essential oil into a cup of steaming hot water and inhale the steam.

Essential Oil:	Promotes:
Bergamot	Restful sleep
Black pepper	Increased alertness
Calendula	Good health
Camphor	Increased energy
Caraway	Increased energy
Catnip	Calmness
Celery	Restful sleep
Chamomile	Sleep and tranquillity
Cinnamon	Increased energy
Clove	Healing
Coriander	Improved memory
Cumin	Immunity
Eucalyptus	Healing
Fennel	Longevity
Gardenia	Feelings of peace
Garlic	Purity of the body

Essential Oil:	Promotes:
Geranium	Happiness
Ginger	Increased energy
Honeysuckle	Weight loss
Hops	Sleep
Hyssop	Purity of the body
Iris	Feelings of love
Jasmine	Love and peace
Juniper	Healing
Lavender	Health
Lemon	Healing and energy
Magnolia	Feelings of love
Marjoram	Sleep
Myrrh	Healing
Narcissus	Feelings of love
Nutmeg	Increased energy
Onion	Immunity
Orange	Joy and energy
Pennyroyal	Increased energy
Pine	Healing
Rose	Love and peace
Rosemary	Longevity
Rue	Calmness
Saffron	Increased energy
Sage	Memory
Thyme	Good health
Vanilla	Sex and love
Yarrow	Increased awareness

PERFUME OILS

Combine the essential oils and allow them to stand for one week before judging the scent. Essential oils are sold by herb suppliers such as "Penn Herb". Small jars and perfume bottles are sold by "Sunburst Bottle Company". See Appendix A for suppliers.

ALPINE BOUQUET

4 drops lavender essential oil
5 drops lemon essential oil
4 drops peppermint essential oil
3 drops rosemary essential oil
4 drops sage essential oil
2 drops thyme essential oil

BAY RUM

15 drops bay essential oil
1 drop orange essential oil
1 drop allspice essential oil

CANDY ROSE

1 teaspoon vanilla essential oil
1 teaspoon rose essential oil

CREAM PERFUME

2 teaspoons essential oil
2 tablespoons beeswax

Melt the wax, add the oil and stir until it cools.

FLOWER BOUQUET

3 drops cinnamon essential oil
7 drops lavender essential oil
10 drops lemon essential oil
7 drops peppermint essential oil
5 drops rosemary essential oil
6 drops sage essential oil

HONEY SOAP SCENT

1 teaspoon lemon essential oil
2 teaspoons rose essential oil
1 teaspoon ginger grass essential oil
1/2 teaspoon rosemary essential oil

HONEY-SCENTED OIL

4 teaspoons citronella essential oil
1 1/2 teaspoons lemon-grass essential oil
3/4 teaspoon cinnamon-leaf essential oil
1/2 teaspoon musk essential oil

ETCHING GLASS

Glasses etched using a wax resist.

Etching dissolves a thin layer of glass that is washed away. The glass beneath the etching is permanently frosted. During the 1800's, etching was done by drawing through a hard, wax ground with a needle and flooding the ground with dangerous acid.

Today there are products designed to etch glass that are easy to use and safe to handle. "Armour Etch" is such a cream. It is sold by stained glass suppliers (see Appendix A) and etches almost any glass in a few minutes.

Before decorating motor vehicle windows, check with the Division of Motor Vehicles to learn which windows may be etched and how much area may be covered.

GENERAL DIRECTIONS

Step 1: Place a can in an electric skillet and set the temperature control at 300 degrees F. Place beeswax in the can to melt. Crude beeswax may be used if it is strained through fine cheesecloth or a nylon stocking.

Step 2: The work area, etching cream and project temperature must be 75 degrees F. or warmer. Place the closed jar of etching cream in very hot water for 10 to 15 minutes. Shake the jar occasionally during this time. The cream is ready to use when all of the crystals are dissolved.

Step 3: Clean the glass with window cleaner to remove all grease, dust and fingerprints. Allow the glass to dry.

Step 4: "Dover Publications" (see Appendix A) sells inexpensive booklets containing stencils and designs. Tape the design on the back of the glass. Turn the glass over and trace the design onto the glass with melted beeswax. Tjantings of different sizes work well as applicators. On page 6 other ways of applying wax are described. If a mistake is made, the wax can be cut away with a sharp blade and the area wiped with a clean cloth. Masking tape or vinyl adhesive can be used to make straight edges and to protect large areas of glass from the etching cream.

Step 5: With a soft brush, apply a thick layer of the etching cream. The cream can be poured onto large areas. Allow the cream to set for 5 minutes. During this time, brush and gently move the cream to make sure there are no bubbles or missed areas. Wash the glass in cold, running tap water to remove the etching cream.

Step 6: Place the glass over a pot of water. Heat the water until the wax melts and can be wiped away with a paper towel. Put the glass through a dishwasher cycle to remove the last traces of wax. Colored foil or fabric may be placed behind the glass to show through the clear sections. Etched glass readily holds paint. Use artist's oil paints, thinned with enough turpentine to make the colors transparent.

ETCHING MIRRORS

The front of mirrors can be etched for a frosted appearance. See page 63 for "Mirror Art" to learn how to remove mirror backings.

ARTIFICIAL STAINED GLASS

Making stained glass is not difficult, but many people are hesitant at the idea of cutting glass and melting lead solder. This formula makes a transparent color to simulate stained glass. It can be washed without damage. Order pattern books from stained glass suppliers. Find denatured alcohol where paint supplies are sold. Shellac and dye are sold by "Woodworker's Supply" (Appendix A).

GENERAL DIRECTIONS

Step 1: Make the following formula.

1 ounce (weight) blonde shellac
1/4 cup denatured alcohol
Alcohol-soluble aniline dye

Place the ingredients in a glass or plastic jar (no metal) and shake it frequently until most of the shellac is dissolved. Let the jar stand for 12 hours. Shake the jar until no sediment is in the bottom. Strain the mixture through nylon and wait about 30 minutes for bubbles to rise out of the mixture.

Step 2: "Vic's Crafts" (see Appendix A) sells a special black outline paste that simulates lead lines of stained glass. Any black acrylic paint can be used for the same effect. Use bottles or tubes that can apply a line of paint about 1/8-inch wide and about 1/16-inch high. Apply the lines before coloring the glass.

A more realistic look is obtained by applying adhesive lead strips before coloring the glass. Such strips are sold by Decra-Led Ltd., Post Office Box 217, Portage, WI 53901, (608) 742-2549.

Step 3: Paint the glass with the solution and let it dry. Clean the brushes in denatured alcohol. Additional coats may be applied, if desired.

WAX RUB-ON STENCILS

Stained glass suppliers (see Appendix A) sell decorative wax stencils. These stencils are placed over glass and rubbed to apply the wax resist.

Etching projects could include: terrariums, glassware, patio doors, fireplace doors, display cases, tinted glass, wine bottles, glass table tops, storm doors, glass plates, spice jars, fish tanks, shower doors, serving dishes, cabinet doors, ash trays, glass lamps, jelly jars, greenhouse windows, mirror fronts, tempered glass, car windows, beveled glass and stained glass.

FLOORS

DUST-LAYING OIL

Spray concrete or wooden floors with this mixture to keep down dust.

4 ounces (weight) clean or crude beeswax (See page 83.)
3 1/2 cups water
2 tablespoons lye (sodium hydroxide)

Read the precautions of handling lye on page 93. Dissolve the lye in 1 cup water. Melt the wax in the remaining water. Boil the two mixtures together until they are well mixed. Strain the mixture through cheesecloth or nylon stocking. Some drain cleaners are 100% lye. Order sodium hydroxide from "Chem Lab" (see Appendix A).

SQUEAKY FLOOR BOARDS

Pour melted wax or liquid furniture polish into the cracks between squeaky floor boards to stop the squeaking.

WAX AND POLISH

Floors covered in tile, marble, linoleum, or sealed wood require the same polish. (See page 79 for "Polish".)

WAX SPILLS

Steel wool soap pads and pot scrubbers made of plastic work well to remove drops of wax from floors and counter tops.

FLOWERS

WATER FOR FRESH FLOWERS

Stir this formula into plain water to make freshly cut flowers last longer.

5 drops silver nitrate
1/4 cup honey

Mix the ingredients and bottle the mixture. Attach a label to the bottle and write on the label the rate of dilution ("Use 1 teaspoon to 1 quart water."). Do not dilute the solution until time for it to be used. Silver nitrate is available from chemical suppliers such as "Chem Lab" and "Hagenow Laboratories" (see Appendix A for suppliers).

WAXED PAPER WINDOW GEMS

Arrange pressed flowers between two sheets of waxed paper. A string for hanging may be looped and placed between the sheets. Set an iron on medium heat and press the sheets to seal them.

WAXING FRESH FLOWERS

Use freshly cut flowers that are free of moisture. Fuzzy or delicate flowers do not respond well to wax dipping. Dip the chosen flowers into 160 degree F. wax. The cooler the wax, the thicker the coating. Hold the flowers by the stem and dip them one at a time. Move them about in the wax to get rid of bubbles.

FOOD PRODUCTS

CANNED CAKES

See the photograph on page 18. Technically, any cake can be baked in tapered, wide-mouth canning jars. When they are removed from the oven, a canning lid is applied. As the cake cools, a hermetic seal forms. Canned cakes may be stored in a pantry with other canned foods or placed in a freezer.

General Directions: Grease and flour tapered, wide-mouth pint canning jars. The jars must be tapered and have no shoulders in order for the cake to release properly after it is baked. Avoid getting grease, flour and batter on the jar rims. Half fill the jars (3/4 to 1 cup of batter in each jar). Bake the cakes at 300 degrees F. for 60 minutes or until a wooden pick inserted in the center comes out clean.

When the cakes are done, quickly remove one hot jar at a time and clean the sealing edge. Immediately apply and firmly tighten a two-piece wide-mouth canning lid. The lid will form a seal as the jar cools. The bread is safe to eat as long as the jar remains sealed and the cake free of mold.

CARAMEL FOOD COLORING

Heat destroys the sweetening power of honey used in this food coloring. A few drops color food items such as gravy, frosting, vinegar or soft drink. Depending on the amount used, the color ranges from golden yellow to dark brown.

1 tablespoon honey
2 tablespoons water
2 tablespoons 100-proof vodka

Microwave the honey in a clear, heat-proof container that will hold at least two cups until it bubbles and blackens (about 3 minutes). Add the water, microwave 30 seconds, and stir. Bottle the liquid, add the vodka and shake well.

CHEESE--See page 21.

CHEWY BARS

These bars will last 6 months or more when stored in an air-tight tin.

1 1/3 cups honey
3/4 cup sugar
3 tablespoons butter
2 cups sifted all-purpose flour
1 teaspoon baking powder
1/2 teaspoon baking soda
1/2 cup blanched almonds
1/4 cup chopped, candied cherries
1/4 cup chopped, candied orange peel
1/4 teaspoon ginger
1/2 teaspoon cardamom
2 teaspoons cinnamon
1/8 teaspoon cloves
2 cups additional flour

In a large saucepan, heat the honey, sugar and butter until the butter is melted. Combine 2 cups flour, baking powder, soda and spices in a bowl and mix well. Add this to the melted mixture and stir well. Mix in the candied fruits and almonds. Add the last 2 cups of flour and mix well. This mixture will be sticky and is enough for one 8-by-8-inch plus one 10 1/2-by-15 1/2-inch cake pan. Smear the dough into the pans and bake about 25 minutes in a preheated 350-degree oven. Cut it into squares and let it cool. The bars will be hard. Allow them to age 1 week in an air-tight tin. The bars will soften, become chewy, and the flavors will blend.

CHOCOLATE COATING

This mixture "strings" well to form swirls on top of the dipped item.

1 ounce beeswax
12 ounces real semi-sweet chocolate

Melt the wax and chocolate in a double boiler. Dip fruit, frozen squares of cake, potato chips, or candy centers into the melted mixture. Place the items on a rack to cool and harden, then store them in an air-tight container.

EGGNOG OR ICE CREAM

Many old-fashioned recipes for eggnog and ice cream include raw eggs. The American Egg Board and the Egg Nutrition Center advise against eating raw or under cooked eggs because of the chance of salmonella poisoning. The following is "safe" recipe for eggnog may also be used for homemade ice cream.

2 cups milk
8 large eggs
1/8 teaspoon salt
1 cup honey
1 teaspoon ground cinnamon
1/2 teaspoon ground nutmeg
1/2 teaspoon ground cloves
1 1/2 teaspoons vanilla
2 cups heavy cream

Heat the milk in a double boiler to 180 degrees F. Beat the eggs and add the salt and honey. Beat about 1 cup of the hot milk into the egg mixture. Add the egg mixture to the remaining hot milk in the saucepan. Cook over low heat, stirring constantly, until the mixture thickens and reaches 180 degrees F. Stir in the spices and vanilla. Cool the mixture over a large bowl of ice for 10 to 12 minutes. Cover and refrigerate it for 24 hours. Add the cream to the chilled mixture. Drink the delicious eggnog either hot or cold, or transfer the mixture to an ice cream maker and freeze it following the manufacturer's instructions. Garnish each serving with a sprinkling of nutmeg.

HONEY

Honey should not be fed to infants under 1 year of age. For more information on honey, contact The National Honey Board (see Appendix A).

Look for the Honey Bear logo on products containing a substantial amount of honey.

HONEY MUSTARD DRESSING

Serve this as a dressing for mixed greens or fruit salads.

1/2 cup vegetable oil
1/4 cup vinegar
1/4 cup honey
1 tablespoon lemon juice
1 teaspoon dry mustard powder
1/2 teaspoon celery seed
1/4 teaspoon salt
1/4 teaspoon paprika
1/8 teaspoon pepper

Blend the ingredients in a food processor until they are thoroughly combined.

HONEY PASTE

Honey paste is an almond paste substitute. Use it in recipes that require almond paste. Marzipan is an example.

3 cups granulated sugar
3 1/2 cups brown sugar
1 1/2 teaspoons baking soda
1 1/2 teaspoons salt
3/4 cup corn syrup
1 cup honey
3/4 cup hot water
1 cup butter
1 cup margarine

Mix all ingredients, except the margarine. Stir in the margarine and mix until a smooth paste is obtained. If the mixture is too thick, add a little more margarine.

HONEY JELLY

Some types of honey crystallize readily. Honey jelly doesn't crystallize and it is not as sweet as pure honey. Honey jelly takes about one week to "set" well. Don't think it is too thin and discard it.

3 cups (2 1/4 pounds) honey
1 cup water
1 foil pouch liquid fruit pectin

Measure the honey and water into a 6-to-8-quart saucepan; mix well. Place the pan over high heat and, while stirring constantly, bring the contents to a full boil. At once, stir in the fruit pectin and again bring the mixture to a full rolling boil. Boil hard 1 minute, stirring constantly. Remove the jelly from the heat and skim off any foam with a metal spoon. Pour it quickly into hot sterilized jars, leaving a 1/4-inch head space. Wipe the jar rims and adjust the lids. Process it in a boiling water bath for 15 minutes (start timing when the water boils). Makes 4 cups.

Herbal Honey Jelly: Pour 1 1/2 cups boiling water over 1/4 cup finely snipped fresh herbs. Let this stand 5 minutes and then strain it. Substitute the herbal water as directed in the basic recipes. Food coloring to match the herb is optional. Mint jelly colored green and rose geranium jelly colored red are examples.

"Less Sweet" Honey Jelly: Use 3/4 cup water and 1/4 cup fresh lemon juice instead of 1 cup water in the basic recipe.

MUSTARD

Bright yellow "hot dog mustard" should not be considered the basic mustard for cooking. Dijon-style mustard is superior because of its ability to enhance many flavors. For gifts, put the mustard in pretty jars and attach the recipe. "Sunburst Bottle Company" (see Appendix A) sells many suitable jars. Dry mustard powder is found in the grocer's spice section.

Vinegar leaches molecules from iron and aluminum. Use plastic, glass, enamel or stainless steel utensils and containers to make and store mustard. Newly prepared mustard is at its most pungent (hot) state. If this degree of pungency is agreeable, refrigerate the mustard at this point. For a milder mustard, allow it to age. To age mustard, place it in a cool (70 to 80 degrees F.), dark place until the taste is agreeable. After aging, refrigerate mustard to retain its flavor.

The shelf life of mustard is indefinite. No matter what its age, mustard will not grow mold, mildew, or harmful bacteria. It may dry out, lose its flavor or turn brown from oxidation, but even then it is safe to eat. If it dries out, just add dry wine or vinegar to reconstitute it.

BASIC DIJON-STYLE MUSTARD

2 cups dry wine
1 large onion, chopped
3 cloves garlic, pressed
1 cup (4 ounces) dry mustard powder
3 tablespoons honey
1 tablespoon oil
2 teaspoons salt

Combine the wine, onion and garlic in a saucepan. Heat to boiling and simmer 5 minutes. Strain the mixture, discard the solids and let it cool. Add the liquid to the dry mustard and stir until smooth. Blend in the honey, oil and salt. While stirring, heat the mustard over low heat until it thickens. Allow the mixture to cool and place it in a covered jar. Age the mustard 6 to 8 weeks, or to an agreeable pungency, and refrigerate it.

Dijon-style Variations: To create variations, use 1 cup of the "Basic Dijon-style Mustard" and add one of the following.

♦ **Honey Dijon:** Add 1/2 cup honey.

♦ **Hot Honey Mustard:** Add 3/4 cup dry mustard powder and 1/2 cup honey.

♦ **Citrus Mustard:** Add 1 tablespoon lemon, lime OR orange juice and 1 tablespoon honey.

♦ **Jalapeno Mustard:** Add 2 tablespoons canned jalapeno peppers (chopped) and 1 tablespoon juice from the can.

♦ **Dried Herb Mustard;** Add 1 tablespoon of dill weed, lemon thyme, rosemary, tarragon OR basil.

CHAMPAGNE MUSTARD

1 cup dry mustard powder
1/4 cup honey
1/2 teaspoon salt
6 ounces flat champagne
1 tablespoon fresh lemon juice

Mix the ingredients in a food processor or blender. Seal the mustard, age it 3 to 4 weeks and refrigerate it.

CHINESE HOT MUSTARD

1 cup dry mustard powder
1/4 teaspoon corn oil
2 tablespoons honey
1/2 cup water

Combine the ingredients and mix well. Seal the mustard in jars. Age it 2 to 4 weeks at room temperature and then refrigerate it.

HORSERADISH MUSTARD

1 cup dry mustard powder
1/4 cup honey
1/2 teaspoon salt
1/2 cup vinegar
1/4 cup oil
1 tablespoon fresh lemon juice
1/4 teaspoon grated lemon zest
5 tablespoons horseradish

Mix the ingredients in a food processor. Seal the mustard and age it 2 to 8 weeks. Refrigerate the mustard when the pungency is agreeable.

WHOLE-SEED MUSTARD

1/2 cup whole, brown mustard seed
3/4 cup dry wine
1 cup dry mustard powder
1/4 cup honey
1/4 teaspoon salt

Place the seed and the wine in a food processor and let them stand for 3 hours. Add the dry mustard, honey and salt.

Blend the mustard and seal it in jars. Age the mustard 2 to 8 weeks at room temperature and then refrigerate it.

PEMMICAN

This mixture is rich and compact, keeping well for several weeks. It is good for snacks and hiking trips, and it makes a good sandwich.

2 cups mixed nuts
1 1/2 cups raisins
8 ounces (weight) dried dates
8 ounces (weight) dried beef or jerky
Salt to taste
Honey

Grind the ingredients through a coarse blade. Mix thoroughly. Add enough honey to make the mixture the consistency of stiff dough. Place the mixture in a plastic bag.

SUBSTITUTING HONEY FOR SUGAR WHEN BAKING

♦ Substitute honey for up to one-half of the sugar. With experimentation, honey can be substituted for all the sugar in some recipes.

♦ Reduce the amount of liquid in the recipe by 1/4 cup for each cup of honey used.

♦ Add about 1/2 teaspoon baking soda for each cup of honey.

♦ Reduce oven temperature by 25 degrees F. to prevent over-browning.

♦ Items baked with honey taste even better after 24 hours.

VANILLA EXTRACT SUPREME

1 ounce (weight) vanilla beans
1 cup 80-proof vodka
1/4 cup honey
2 tablespoons almond extract

Cut the vanilla beans into small pieces and bruise them. Bottle the beans with the vodka and let this stand for 2 weeks. Heat the closed bottle in a 170 degree F. oven for 3 hours. Shake the bottle every 30 minutes. Oven temperatures vary greatly. It is wise to use an oven thermometer and check it often to be sure the proper temperature is maintained.

Strain the liquid through a coffee filter or a paper towel. Add the honey and almond extract. Mix this well and let it stand 2 days. Siphon or pour the vanilla off the sediment.

WAX COATING FOR FRUIT

Fresh fruit and vegetables are less likely to wither if a thin film of wax is applied to their surfaces.

Parts by weight:
2 parts beeswax
1 part carnauba wax
.75 part soap
26 parts water

Combine the ingredients and boil until the waxes are melted and the soap is dissolved. Cool the mixture to 160 degrees F. and immerse the fruit for 10 to 30 seconds.

A "super" is the top box of a beehive.

HAIR PRODUCTS

BEARD SOFTENER

2 tablespoons sodium lauryl sulfate
2 tablespoons glycerin
1 tablespoon honey
2 cups distilled water

Mix the ingredients and shake well. Sodium lauryl sulfate is a detergent and a surfactant available from "Chem Lab" (see Appendix A). Apply the beard softener, wait a few minutes, and shave when the beard is softened.

BEARD WAX

Ounces by weight:
1 ounce purified turpentine spirits
1 ounce pure olive oil
3 ounces beeswax
1 ounce petroleum jelly
1/2 ounce Peru balsam
Fragrant essential oil (optional)

Melt the wax. Add the remaining ingredients and melt again. Pour the mixture into a small container and stir until it cools. Pure olive oil and Peru balsam are sold by "Penn Herb". Purified turpentine and olive oil are sold by "Chem Lab" (see Appendix A).

CONDITIONER

Of all fatty substances, lanolin is most similar to that from the scalp. See page 89 for "Skin Cream". Rub a tiny amount of the cream between the palms and run it through dry hair. The hair should be shiny and healthy-looking. If too much cream is applied the hair will look greasy.

HAIR POMADE

Pomades are probably the oldest method used by men to control curly hair. Pomades remove curliness by the mechanical means of plastering hair against the scalp.

1 ounce (weight) beeswax
4 ounces (weight) lanolin
Fragrant essential oil (optional)

Melt the beeswax and add the lanolin and essential oil. Stir until the mixture cools.

PRESSING OIL

Hot pressing to straighten hair was introduced in 1910. The oil is a heat transfer medium and a lubricant for hot combing. The heat breaks some of the intermolecular bonds within the hair and permits it to straighten.

1 ounce (weight) beeswax
24 ounces (weight) petroleum jelly
Fragrant essential oil (optional)

Melt the beeswax in a microwave or double boiler. Add the petroleum jelly and melt again. Stir well. Use pressing oil after shampooing and towel drying the hair.

SHAMPOO

Raw honey contains tiny wax particles that makes hair shine without oiliness. Obtain the benefits of honey shampoo by adding 2 tablespoons of raw honey to each cup of ordinary shampoo.

SHAMPOO AND CONDITIONER

1/2 teaspoon beeswax
1 tablespoon honey
2 cups ordinary shampoo

Melt the beeswax and stir in the honey and shampoo. If the mixture is not perfectly smooth, heat it until it can be mixed properly. Shampoo as usual.

SHAVING CREAM (LATHERLESS)

Latherless shaving cream contains no soap and is good for sensitive skin and for people who have a problem with ingrown hair. The formulation is the same as "Skin Cream" (see page 89). Apply the cream to dry skin and shave when the hair is softened.

SHAVING PASTE

6 ounces (weight) powdered soap
2 tablespoons honey
1 tablespoon water
Fragrant essential oil (optional)

Melt the ingredients in a double boiler.

HERBS AND HONEY

Honey is effective against the growth of common pathogenic organisms that grow at the site of wounds. In one study, honey was used to dress the ulcer wounds of 59 patients. In 58 patients, there was no growth of micro-organisms at the site of the wounds and the wounds were dehydrated after one week. Additional invitro studies have shown the effectiveness of honey in inhibiting the growth of bacteria such as *Salmonella* and *E. Coli.* Fructose, the predominant sugar in honey, is very hygroscopic. This, along with the anti-bacterial properties of honey, makes honey an excellent skin treatment.

The honey is considered an active ingredient in the following herbal remedies. These natural herbal remedies are for everyday problems. Just because herbs are natural substances doesn't mean they can be used indiscriminately. Herbs can be strong medicine. Never exceed the recommended dose. If the problem becomes severe or persists for more than a week, it is advisable to see a physician.

See Appendix A for herb suppliers and page 28 for "Essential Oils".

WARNING: Children, pregnant women and anyone taking drugs (over-the-counter or prescription) should not take herbal remedies without the direction of a physician.

The American Botanical Council and The Herb Research Foundation publish "Herbalgram", an excellent review of the latest developments in botanical medicine. To subscribe, call 1-800-748-2617.

The American Botanical Council
Post Office Box 201660
Austin, Texas 78720

The Herb Research Foundation
1007 Pearl Street, Suite 200
Boulder, Colorado 80302

BURNS

♦ Pure honey is good for minor burns.

♦ A mixture of equal parts aloe gel and honey relieves pain and promotes healing of burns.

♦ A mixture of 1 teaspoon juice from crushed ginger root and 1 tablespoon honey relieves the hot, stinging sensation.

COLDS, COUGHS AND FLU

♦ Use 1 to 2 drops eucalyptus essential oil in a cup of boiling water sweetened with honey. Drink the mixture and breathe the vapor to clear clogged nasal passages.

♦ Cayenne tea reduces the discomfort caused by colds and helps warm the body. Use 1 teaspoon dried herb and 2 tablespoons honey in 1 cup hot water.

♦ Fenugreek tea is a good expectorant and is also soothing to sore throats. Use 1 teaspoon dried herb and 1/4 cup honey in 1 cup hot water.

♦ Goldenseal powder relieves congestion and is soothing to inflamed mucous membranes. Mix 1 teaspoon goldenseal powder and 1/4 cup honey in 2 cups boiling water. Let it cool. Take 2 teaspoons up to 6 times daily.

♦ Mullein tea is wonderful for dry, nagging coughs. Use 1 tablespoon dried mullein and 2 tablespoons honey in 1 cup hot water. Drink 2 cups daily.

GAS AND INDIGESTION

♦ Basil is good for a gassy stomach. Mix 1 teaspoon of dried basil and 1 tablespoon honey in 1/2 cup warm water. Strain it and drink 2 cups daily.

♦ Catnip is antispasmodic. It calms stomach cramps and aids relaxation. Mix 1 teaspoon catnip extract and 2 tablespoons honey in 1 cup water. Drink 2 cups daily.

♦ Chamomile tea is good for indigestion and has a calming effect. Mix 1 tablespoon dried chamomile and 2 tablespoons honey in 1 cup boiling water. Drink 1 cup nightly.

HICCUPS

♦ Mix 1/2 teaspoon honey with 1/2 teaspoon sugar. Swallow this to increase the body's carbon dioxide level.

SKIN HEALING

Warning: Stop all bleeding before applying honey to broken skin.

♦ A mixture of equal parts aloe gel and honey promotes healing of wounds.

♦ A mixture of 2 tablespoons honey to 1/2 cup arnica lotion promotes healing of wounds. Use daily, only on unbroken skin.

♦ Calendula ointment is soothing to skin wounds and bruises.

♦ Comfrey ointment promotes healing of scrapes, cuts and other skin wounds.

♦ Mix 2 tablespoons honey and 1/2 cup witch hazel. Apply this mixture to skin to soothe inflammations.

HERBAL OINTMENT

Ounces by weight:
4 ounces dry, powdered herb
6 ounces fat or oil
1 tablespoon honey
1 ounce beeswax

The fat and oil can be cocoa butter, lanolin, mineral oil or vegetable shortening. Place ingredients in a 200 degree F. oven for 3 hours. Strain the ointment and store it in a tightly sealed tin or wide-mouth jar. Stop all bleeding, apply the herbal ointment and a bandage. Repeat the treatment daily for 3 days.

SLEEP

♦ Drink a cup of chamomile tea sweetened with honey.

SORE THROATS

♦ Fenugreek gargle is excellent for sore, irritated throats. Use 20 drops of extract and 3 tablespoons honey in 1 cup water. Gargle 3 times daily.

♦ Marshmallow root tea is soothing for scratchy, itchy throats. Use 1 teaspoon dried herb and 3 tablespoons honey in 1 cup hot water. Drink up to 3 cups daily.

SUNBURN

♦ Add honey to chamomile tea, aloe gel or witch hazel. Gently apply the mixture on the burned area.

HERBS AND THE BEES

The following herbs attract bees to the garden.

Bee balm
Borage
Chamomile
Catnip
Fennel
Germander
Hyssop
Lavender
Lemon Balm
Marjoram
Mints
Oregano
Sage
Sacred basil
Thyme
Winter savory

HIGHLIGHT CREAM

"Highlight Cream" is a unique cream used to apply decorative metallic finishes to wax, wood, glass plastic, plaster, fabric, metal, paper and leather. Simply apply the cream and when it is dry, rub and buff.

Tiny amounts of artist's dry pigments can be added to "Highlight Cream" to produce a metallic finish in any color. See page 84 of "Sealing Wax" to read about bronze powder and dry pigments.

1 teaspoon beeswax
2 teaspoons turpentine
2 teaspoons bronze powder

Melt the beeswax. Separately, mix the turpentine and the bronze powder. Add the melted beeswax and stir until the mixture is smooth. If the wax lumps, it may be necessary to heat the mixture over boiling water and stir until it is smooth.

Caution: Bronze powder is metal. Never put it in a microwave.

To use the cream, stroke a fingertip over it to pick up a very small amount. Rut it evenly and thinly over smooth surfaces or raised designs. Wait a minute for the cream to dry and gently buff it with a soft cloth. The cream may be thinned with turpentine and applied to recesses with a brush.

Notes and Clippings

HONEY BEAR

This bear is wondering if the honeybee on his nose means trouble.

EQUIPMENT AND SUPPLIES

- ❑ Electric glue gun
- ❑ Tan-colored hot glue sticks
- ❑ Stuffed bear
- ❑ Honey pot and dipper
- ❑ Artificial honeybees

Electric hot glue guns are sold by craft suppliers. Artificial honeybees are sold by some beekeeping suppliers and candle-making suppliers. Tan-colored hot glue sticks are sometimes difficult to locate. They can be ordered from "Woodworker's Supply" (see Appendix A) or use clear sticks. After the glue cools, color it with a yellow felt-tipped marker.

GENERAL DIRECTIONS

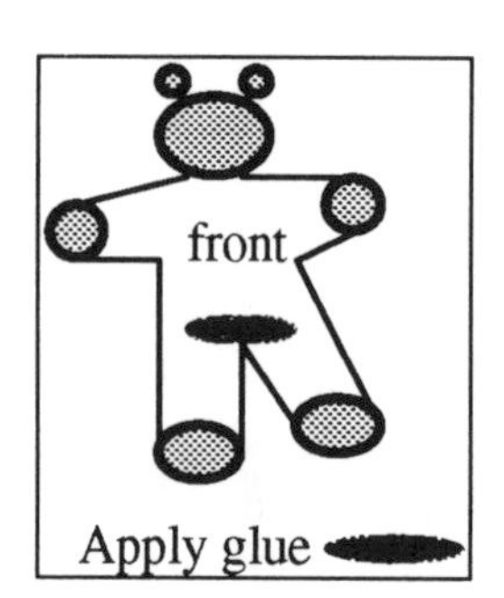

Step 1: Buy a stuffed bear with arms and legs that bend or follow the directions at the end of this section to make a bear. Apply hot glue to the front of the bear as shown. Hold the bear in a sitting position until the glue cools.

Step 2: Try different arrangements of the bear, honey pot and dipper until a pleasing one is found. Apply hot glue to make the arrangement permanent.

Step 3: Use hot glue to make honey inside the pot. Make the dripping honey by applying hot glue in one spot. It will drip naturally. Don't worry about mistakes when applying the glue. Honey bears are messy eaters. Glue on one or more artificial honeybees.

HONEY BEAR PATTERN

This pattern for a stuffed bear looks too simple to believe, but it really does work.

Step 1: Enlarge the pattern to the size desired. Measure the pattern to determine the amount of fur needed. Lay the pattern on the wrong side of the fur, making sure the arrows follow the nap. Cut one front piece, flip the pattern over and cut another front piece. Place the straight edge of the back piece along a fold and cut one piece from the fur.

Step 2: Insert the eyes. Sew the two front pieces together from the top of the head, along the stomach, to the crotch.

Step 3: Place the front and back pieces together. Start at one of the notches at the crotch and machine stitch all around the bear to the opposite notch.

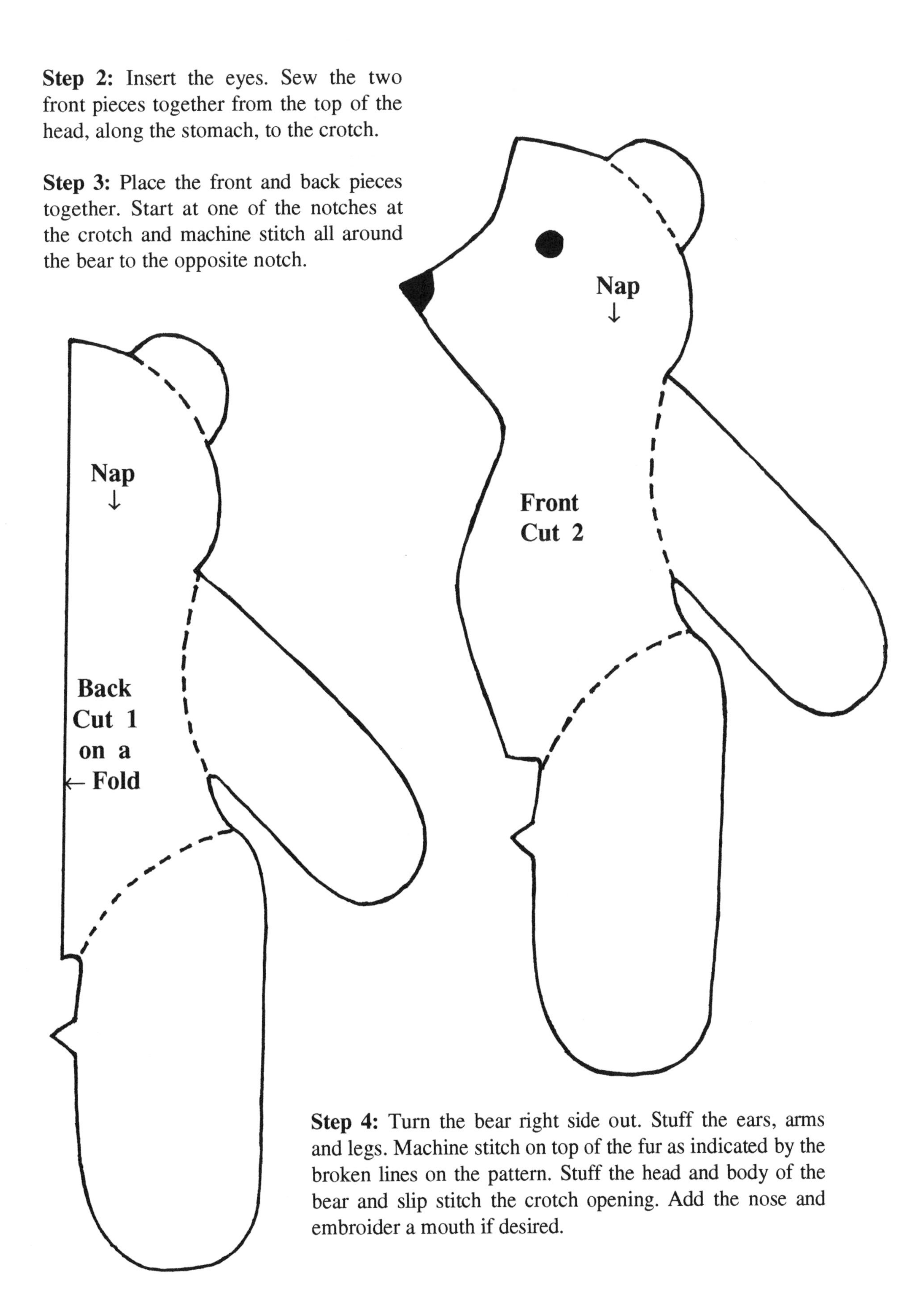

Step 4: Turn the bear right side out. Stuff the ears, arms and legs. Machine stitch on top of the fur as indicated by the broken lines on the pattern. Stuff the head and body of the bear and slip stitch the crotch opening. Add the nose and embroider a mouth if desired.

JUDGING APIARY PRODUCTS

Beekeepers are proud of their products and often exhibit them in competition with one another. A superior quality product and knowledge of the show requirements are required. Honey shows teach beekeepers how to prepare honey to top standards. If honey is good enough for the show bench, then it is good enough for the store shelf. Below each product narrative is a scale of points used for judging. Note that scoring methods may vary among judges.

BEESWAX

High quality beeswax is straw to canary yellow in color. It should be free of dirt, honey and propolis. It should be free of cracks, layering and shrinkage (indicated by a concave surface). The wax must be uniform and have a pleasant odor. It should not be greasy or sticky, which is sometimes caused by wax release agents. Most shows require the wax to weigh at least two pounds.

Beeswax:	
Color	30
Cleanliness	35
Uniformity of appearance	20
Freedom from cracking and shrinkage	15
Total Points	**100**

COMB HONEY

Comb honey should be capped with new cappings that are white, clean and unsoaked by honey. Section comb honey in round sections should have all cells capped. Wooden sections may have the outermost rows of cells uncapped. All cells should be of uniform height and filled with high quality honey. The wood or plastic should be free of dirt, propolis and bits of wax.

Comb Honey:	
Quality and uniformity of sections	5
Cleanliness of sections	20
Completeness of fill	20
Completeness of capping	10
Cleanliness and appearance of cappings	20
Quality and flavor	10
Uniformity of comb sections, including honey	15
Total Points	**100**

CREAMED HONEY

The appearance, suitability and uniformity of the containers is important, but texture is probably the most important factor in judging creamed honey. It should have crystals fine enough not to be felt on the tongue. No solidified foam or extraneous material should be on the surface. The honey should be spreadable but not so soft that it runs off a knife. Flavor and aroma are also important considerations. Ties in judging creamed honey are broken in favor of the honey with the finer texture.

Creamed Honey:	
Appearance and uniformity of containers	5
Uniform level of fill	5
Color	5
Firmness of set	15
Freedom from foreign material	15
Freedom from froth and frosting	15
Uniformity of honey entry including texture	10
Flavor and aroma	10
Texture of granulation (smooth and fine)	20
Total Points	**100**

CUT COMB OR CHUNK HONEY

Chunk honey and cut comb honey should contain neatly cut, fully capped combs which fill their containers completely to the fill line. Pieces of comb should all be oriented the same way in the container. The liquid honey surrounding chunk combs should show all the characteristics of good extracted honey and have no bits of wax from the comb floating in it.

Cut Comb or Chunk Honey	
Cleanliness and appearance	5
Uniformity and neatness of comb edges	20
Completeness of fill of comb	20
Cleanliness and appearance of cappings	20
Cut Comb Continued	
Completeness of cappings	10
Quality and flavor	10
Uniformity of combs	15
Total Points	**100**

LIQUID HONEY

The moisture should be between 15.5 and 16.5 percent. Jars should be suitable, uniform and cleaned with great care. Any trace of oil, detergent or soap will appear on top of the honey by the time it reaches the exhibit. Many jars have a line indicating their fill level. Avoid jars that have bubbles in the glass. Each jar should be filled to the same height. The air space should not be visible when the lid is in place and the jar is standing upright. Caps must be clean inside and out. High quality extracted honey has a characteristic sparkle of cleanliness when held up to the light. Ties in judging liquid honey are broken in favor of the lightest colored honey. If a tie still exists, it is broken in favor of the honey with the lower moisture content.

Liquid Honey	
Appearance and uniformity of containers	5
Uniform level of fill	5
Color	5
Freedom from crystals	15
Freedom from foreign material	15
Freedom from air bubbles	15
Uniformity of honey	5
Flavor and aroma	10
Density	15
Brightness	10
Total Points	**100**

LEATHER

INSTANT SHOE SHINE

1/4 cup petroleum jelly (See page 77.)
1/4 cup turpentine or mineral spirits

Melt the petroleum jelly in a microwave. Remove it from the heat and stir in the turpentine. Wear thick rubber gloves and saturate a sponge in the mixture. Tightly wring out the sponge and set it on a rack to dry for 2 days. Rub the sponge over shoes for an instant shine. The sponge is effective for several months.

LEATHER SOFTENER

With age and exposure, leather such as work shoes, hunting boots and baseball gloves becomes hard. This formula softens leather and makes it waterproof.

1 ounce (weight) beeswax
8 ounces (weight) petroleum jelly

Melt the ingredients in a microwave or double boiler. Brush the hot mixture onto the leather and allow it to penetrate. If possible, place the item in hot sun to help the mixture penetrate the leather. Polish the leather with a cloth to remove excess waterproofing. Also see page 102.

RAZOR STROP PREPARATION

Parts by weight:
1 part aluminum oxide powder
1 part tin oxide powder
1 part petroleum jelly
1 part beeswax

Melt the wax and petroleum jelly in a microwave or double boiler. Remove it from heat and stir in the dry ingredients. Tin and aluminum oxide are sold by "Hagenow Laboratories" and "Chem Lab" (see Appendix A).

SADDLE SOAP

The formulation of saddle soap is the same as "Skin Cream" (see page 89). Once leather is treated with saddle soap, it doesn't accept polish very well.

SHOE POLISH

There is no difference between polish for sealed wood and that for polished leather. Coloring the formula helps cover scuff marks. More formulas are listed under "Polish" (see page 79).

3 ounces (weight) beeswax
1/2 ounce (weight) carnauba wax
1/2 cup mineral spirits
1 tablespoon soap
1/2 cup water
Oil-soluble aniline dye or lampblack

Melt the waxes in a microwave or double boiler. Dissolve the soap in hot water. Dissolve the dye in the turpentine. Remove the wax from heat and stir in the turpentine and dye mixture. Stir in the soap water mixture. Stir it until it cools (at least 108 degrees F.) and pour it into tins. Lampblack is sold by "Hagenow Laboratories" and aniline dyes are sold by wood-finishing suppliers such as "Woodworker's Supply" (see Appendix A).

WATERPROOFING

See page 102.

LIQUEURS

The names *cordial, ratafia* and *liqueur* are interchangeable. Their common characteristics are sweetness and alcohol content. Liqueurs are served at room temperature in very small glasses as dessert or after-dinner drinks. They are used in mixed drinks and for flavoring food. Liqueurs are easily made. Their flavor comes from herbs, spices, fruits, nuts or bottled extracts. It is illegal to sell liqueurs without a license.

EXTRACTS

Extracts designed to flavor liqueurs are listed by most wine-making suppliers (see Appendix A). Honey may be substituted for sugar in extract recipes as long as the honey taste does not interfere with the flavor. Substitute 1 1/4 cups honey for each cup of sugar. It is unlawful to copy liqueurs and call them by their trade names, but with this chart and the instructions that come with each bottle of extract, commercial liqueurs can be imitated.

Extract Name	Trade Name Likeness ®
Reverendine	B & B
Orange Triple Dry	Cointreau
Lorbuis	Drambuie
Yellow Genepy	Galliano
Dantzig	Goldwasser
Orange Brandy	Grand Mariner
Moka	Kahlua
Irish Glen	Irish Mist
Cafe Sport	Tia Maria
Chocolate Mint	Vandermint

MEAD EXTRACT

1 teaspoon lemon essential oil
1/4 teaspoon clove essential oil
1/4 teaspoon cinnamon essential oil
1/8 teaspoon nutmeg essential oil
1/8 teaspoon ginger essential oil
5 drops allspice essential oil
7 drops sassafras essential oil
5 fluid ounces 80-proof vodka

Use food grade essential oils available from herb suppliers such as "Penn Herb" (see Appendix A). Combine the oils and vodka and let them stand for 1 week. Shake the bottle occasionally.

LIQUEURS FROM SCRATCH

Steeping: Steep at room temperature, in glass containers and in a dark place. Mix the ingredients every 2 or 3 days. Fresh ingredients such as fruit should be completely covered with alcohol. Put the fruit in a bag and place a weight over it if necessary.

Filtering: After the suggested steeping time, pour the liquid through a coarse strainer such as cheesecloth or a tea strainer. Filter again through a finer filter such as a coffee filter or paper towel.

Siphoning: Honey and other ingredients sometimes cloud liqueurs. Allow liqueurs to sit undisturbed for a few days and siphon or pour off the clear top solution. Discard the sediment or use it for cooking.

Glycerin: Glycerin adds a feeling of "thickness" to the taste of liqueurs. Add 1 to 3 tablespoons of glycerin per quart liqueur. Glycerin is found in the drug section of department stores.

Coloring: Some extracts contain coloring, but formulas from scratch would benefit from an appropriate food color.

Aging: Liqueurs from extracts are ready to drink as soon as they are mixed. Liqueurs made from fresh ingredients usually improve with age. The shelf life of liqueurs is indefinite.

ALMOND LIQUEUR

2 tablespoons vanilla extract
3 tablespoons almond extract
Zest from 1 lemon
2 cups honey
2 cups 80-proof light rum or vodka

Grate the zest (yellow skin) from the lemon avoiding the white pith. Add the zest and extracts to the rum or vodka. Steep for 1 month. Filter; add honey and stir. Let stand until clear; siphon.

ANISETTE

5 tablespoons anise seed, crushed
1 1/2 teaspoons fennel seed, crushed
1 1/2 teaspoons ground coriander
2 cups honey
3 cups 80-proof brandy

Add seeds to the brandy. Steep 2 to 3 weeks. Filter; add the honey and stir. Let stand until clear; siphon.

CREME DE MENTHE

1/2 teaspoon peppermint extract
1 cup honey
2 cups vodka
1/8 teaspoon green food coloring

Mix the ingredients. This liqueur can be used as soon as it is mixed. If it is allowed to stand more than a few days, siphoning may be necessary.

CURACAO

Zest of 4 oranges
Pinch of cloves and nutmeg
2 cups honey
3 cups 80-proof bourbon

Grate the zest (orange skin) from 4 oranges. Avoid the white pith. Steep the zest and spices in bourbon for 1 month. Filter; add honey and stir. Let stand until clear; siphon.

FRUIT LIQUEURS

Choose ONE of the following fruits:
2 1/2 pounds peaches,
2 pounds apricots,
or 4 cups cherries or berries.
Add:
Zest of 1 lemon
Pinch of cloves
2 cups honey
3 cups 80-proof rum, brandy or vodka

Use fresh fruit, weighed without stones or pits. Mash the fruit, add the remaining ingredients and steep it 4 to 6 months. Strain to remove the fruit that can be eaten or used in cooking. Save the liquid, let it stand until clear and siphon.

HONEY LIQUEUR

1/2 cup honey
1/2 cup 80-proof white rum or vodka

continued

This liqueur can be used as soon as it is mixed. If it is allowed to stand more than a few days, siphoning may be necessary.

OTHER LIQUEURS

Choose ONE of the following:

- 3/4 teaspoon allspice
- 1/2 teaspoon ginger
- 7 tablespoons fresh mint
- 2 teaspoons dried sage, 1 clove and the zest of 1 lemon
- 2 tablespoons dried melissa and the zest of 1/4 lemon
- 1 tablespoon caraway seed and 1 clove
- 2 1/2 tablespoons chopped licorice root
- 1 teaspoon ground rosemary, 1/4 teaspoon coriander, the zest of 1/2 lemon and 1 mint leaf
- 2 teaspoons coconut extract and 1/2 teaspoon vanilla
- 2 teaspoons chocolate extract and 1/2 teaspoon vanilla

Steep the chosen flavoring in 1 1/2 cups 80-proof rum, brandy or vodka until a pleasing taste is derived (up to 14 days). Filter and discard the solids. Add 3/4 cup honey to the liquid; taste and adjust the sweetness. Let stand until clear; siphon.

POUSSE CAFE (Floating Cordial)

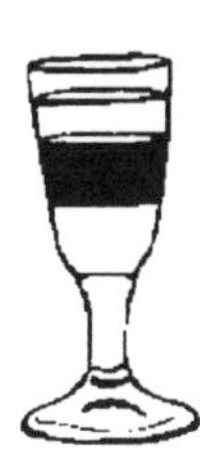

A hydrometer used for wine-making can be used to measure the specific gravity of liqueurs. Note the measurement on the bottle label. The heaviest liqueur has the highest specific gravity. Pour about 1 inch of the heaviest liqueur into a cordial glass. Choose a lighter liqueur (lower specific gravity) of a different color. Pour it slowly over the bottom of an inverted spoon onto the previous liqueur. Beautiful layers of color can be achieved.

LOST WAX INVESTMENT CASTING

Over 4,000 years ago, early man discovered that the wild honey he ate yielded beeswax that could be shaped into forms. He covered the beeswax form in clay and fired the clay to harden it. Wax melted from the clay, leaving its impression. Molten metal was poured into the clay form and allowed to cool. The clay was removed to reveal a perfect metal copy of the "lost" wax form.

Lead's low melting point makes it the most common metal poured at home. It can be melted in an iron pot on any stove. Lead is regarded a dead metal because it doesn't give off dangerous gas when it is melted. Tin and pewter also lend themselves to top-of-the-stove foundry work.

EQUIPMENT AND SUPPLIES

- ☐ Pure lead or lead solder
- ☐ A wax model
- ☐ 5 pounds plaster of Paris
- ☐ Heavy leather or asbestos gloves
- ☐ Iron pot or metal crucible to melt lead
- ☐ Tongs or pliers to handle the crucible
- ☐ Modeling wax to form sprue and risers
- ☐ Hammer to break the mold

The wax model should be about the size of a lemon and can be molded, modeled or carved. Plaster of Paris is sold by craft stores and paint supply stores. Buy lead at building supply stores or ask for free lead from businesses that balance car wheels. "Barker Enterprises" sells lead as mold weights. Lead solder is an alloy made of tin and lead. It is sold by building suppliers and stained glass suppliers. See page 64 for "Modeling Wax" and Appendix A for suppliers.

GENERAL DIRECTIONS

Understanding lead flow: Molten lead tends to travel in a straight line. It will not flow readily around a 90-degree turn and it will not flow backwards toward its source. Lead cools as it enters the mold. The more narrow the space, the more quickly the lead cools. Its force diminishes the further it travels. Sections in the model which are very thin, or sticking out from the bulk of the model should have individual risers. Risers are thin wax rods that permit air to escape when the lead is poured into the mold. Risers should be curved from the model and extend to the top of the plaster mold. It's always better to have too many risers than too few. Clean-up time will be greater, but the chance of failure is reduced. Each model will require different vents or risers. Don't be afraid to experiment. The lead can always be recast.

Step 1: Make a cone-shaped piece of wax from modeling wax or from candle stubs. This piece of wax forms a cup to guide melted lead into the mold. It should be 2 to 3 inches long and attached near the thickest section of the model. See the drawing after Step 2. Heat a metal tool and attach the wax to an inconspicuous place on the model.

Step 2: Make wax risers or vents by rolling modeling wax into thin rods or by dipping yarn into melted beeswax to make wax rods. The yarn is removed later when the wax is melted from the mold. Determine the placement and number of risers. The ends of the risers and the cone-shaped gate must be 1 or 2 inches above the top of the model and equal height. Melt them onto the model. The following drawings suggest the placement.

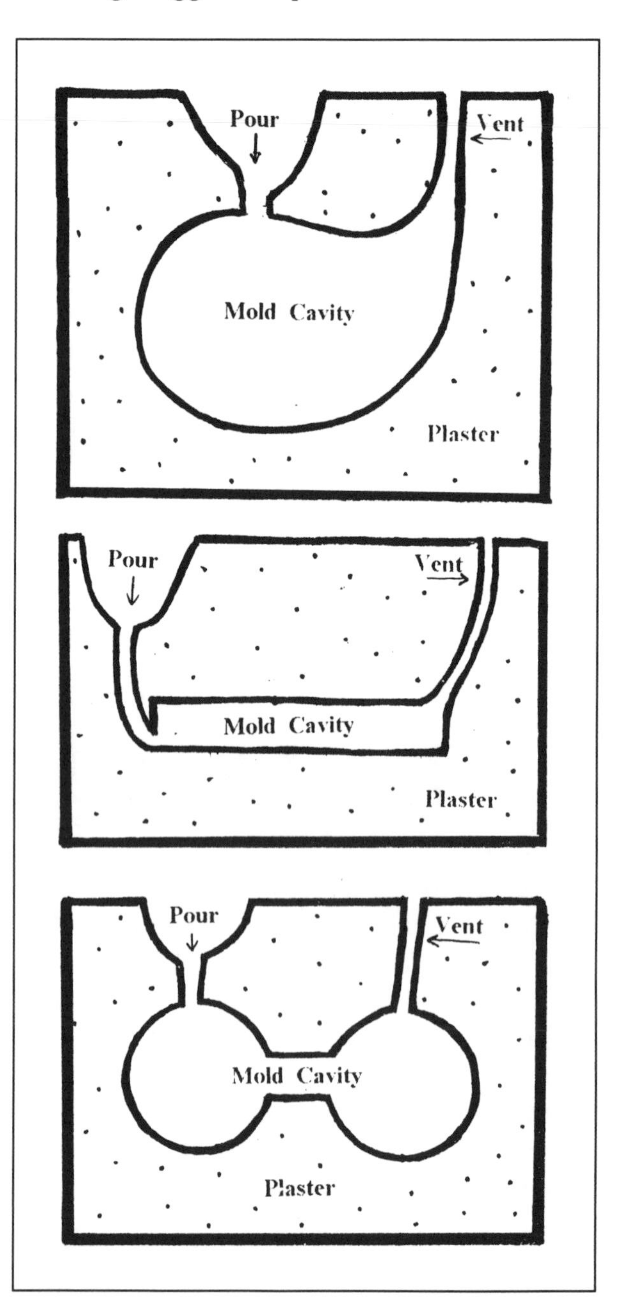

Step 3: With petroleum jelly or silicone spray, lubricate a smooth-sided can or waxed-paper carton that is large enough

to hold the model. Allow at least 2 inches of plaster between the model and the sides of the container.

Step 4: Mix a small amount of plaster of Paris as the package directs and pour 2 to 3 inches of it into the container. Tap the container to release bubbles. Wait 10 to 15 minutes for the plaster to thicken and become firm enough to support the model. Place the model with gate and risers into the container. No part of the gate, risers or wax model should touch the container.

Step 5: Mix more plaster and pour it around the base of the model (never over it) to avoid creating bubbles. Tap the container as the plaster is poured to help release bubbles. Fill the can until nothing but the top of the risers and gate are visible.

Step 6: Wait an hour or two for the plaster to harden. Remove the bottom of the can with a can opener or tear off the paper milk carton. Wait one week for the plaster to dry and harden.

Step 7: Put the plaster in a pot or pie tin with the opening facing down. Place this in a 200 degree F. oven, which is hot enough to melt the wax, but not hot enough to start a fire. If yarn was used to make risers, remove it as soon as the wax melts. Tilt the mold to be sure all wax is released. Empty the pan of melted wax and save it for other purposes.

Step 8: When all wax is melted out of the mold, place the can of plaster with the opening facing up in a bucket of dry sand. Be careful not to get sand inside the mold. Place this in a 225 degree F. oven for 1 hour. Increase the heat to 500 degree F. and maintain it for at least 2 hours. Do not remove the mold from the oven until the lead is ready to pour.

Warning: If the plaster is not perfectly dry, steam will cause molten lead to spurt out of the mold.

Step 9: Wear protective clothing. Goggles and leather boots, apron, and gloves are a necessary precaution. Cut the lead into small pieces and place it in a crucible, a cast iron pot or a large iron ladle. Melt the lead over a gas flame. Carefully lift the pot from the fire with tongs and with an iron bar, skim off or hold back any slag or impurities that are floating on the surface. Pour the lead steadily but quickly until it comes to the top of the opposite vent or riser.

Step 10: Let the casting cool naturally. Do not be tempted to cool it with water or any other method. The casting will shrink slightly as it cools. Break the plaster off the lead with a hammer. Be careful not to hit the lead. Soak the lead model in water to remove the last traces of plaster.

Step 11: Saw or cut the lead risers and sprue away from the model. Clean all plaster from the undercuts. Use a knife, file or sandpaper to clean up the lead. Stained glass suppliers (see Appendix A) sell patinas for lead that produce attractive black, brass or copper finishes.

Step 12: Optional: A rubber mold can be made from the lead model (see page 67 for "Molds: Rubber Latex"). Cast a wax model in the rubber mold. The metal casting process can be repeated, only now an unlimited number of wax reproductions can be cast in metal.

MAKE-UP

Small containers for makeup and lip balm are sold by "Sunburst Bottle Company" (see Appendix A).

ALKANET COLORED OIL

The dried, powdered root of alkanet is used to safely color cosmetics. Mix about 1 tablespoon alkanet root into 1/2 cup mineral oil. Heat the mixture and allow it to cool. Repeat the heating and cooling process until the oil is very dark red. Strain the oil through a coffee filter or a paper towel. This oil can be used to color any formula that requires mineral oil.

EYEBROW PENCILS

Parts by weight:
3 parts beeswax
5 parts mineral oil
7 parts carnauba wax
5 parts lampblack

Combine the ingredients and heat them over boiling water until the mixture is smooth. Pour it into molds. Ingredients are sold by laboratory suppliers such as "Hagenow Laboratories" and "Chem Lab" (see Appendix A).

EYE LINING PENCILS

Follow the above formula for "Eyebrow Pencils" and add more oil to obtain a softer product.

LIP CREAM

Parts by weight:
7 parts "Alkanet Colored Oil"
5 parts beeswax
5 parts spermaceti

The formula for "Alkanet Colored Oil" is listed on this page. Heat the ingredients in a can over boiling water until the mixture is smooth. Pour it into small jars. Spermaceti is sold by "Haussmann's Pharmacy" (see Appendix A).

LIP GLOSS

Simple petroleum jelly is a good clear lip gloss. Lipstick colors this formula. This is a good way to use lipstick that is too dark because the gloss will be a lighter color.

1 teaspoon shredded beeswax
1/2 teaspoon lipstick
1/2 teaspoon petroleum jelly

Melt the ingredients in a small can placed in boiling water. Stir it well and pour it into a small jar.

MASCARA

This type of mascara is molded into bars or cakes. Moisten the mascara with a wet brush and apply it to eyelashes.

Parts by weight:
10 parts lampblack
36 parts beeswax
9 parts carnauba wax
13.5 parts triethanolamine
31.5 parts stearic acid

Mix the ingredients and heat them over boiling water until the mixture is smooth. Pour it into small molds. Ingredients are sold by "Hagenow Laboratories" and "Chem Lab" (see Appendix A).

MASK ADHESIVE

Parts by weight:
17 parts beeswax
8 parts lanolin
5 parts Canada balsam
3 parts castor oil

Melt the beeswax in a microwave or a double boiler. Add the remaining ingredients and heat it until the mixture is smooth. Canada balsam is sold by "Chem Lab" (see Appendix A).

NOSE PUTTY

Ounces by weight:
2 ounces beeswax
2 ounces Canada balsam
1 ounce coconut oil
1 tablespoon powdered alkanet root

Mix the oil and alkanet root. Repeatedly heat the oil and allow it to cool to extract color from the alkanet root. When the oil is sufficiently colored, strain it and add the remaining ingredients. Heat to 190 degrees F. to melt the ingredients. Coconut oil is sold with cooking oils. Alkanet root and beeswax are sold by herb suppliers and Canada balsam is sold by "Chem Lab" (see Appendix A).

THEATRICAL GREASE PAINT

2 tablespoons coconut oil
1 tablespoon beeswax
1 tablespoon lampblack

Grind the lampblack into the oil. Combine the ingredients and melt them in a microwave or a small can placed in boiling water. Stir until the mixture cools. Coconut oil is sold with cooking oils and lampblack is sold by chemical suppliers such as "Hagenow Laboratories" (see Appendix A).

MEAD

It is argued that mead was man's first alcoholic drink and that Bacchus was the god of mead long before becoming known as the god of wine. Often associated with the ancient Greek and Roman empires, mead was gloriously written about by Homer, Virgil and Aristotle. The Argonauts of 235 BC poured mead upon the sea before the anchor was weighed, a custom related to the use of champagne to launch a new ship. The word "honeymoon" comes from an ancient custom of a couple drinking mead in hope of having a son nine months later.

Artwork by permission of Dancing Bear, Inc.

Mead was drunk from *mazers*, ornate bowls or goblets with two or more handles. Often the mazer was a communion cup passed from person to person, each offering a prayer or pledge before drinking. Old English "*waes hael*" meant "be of good health" and the mazer became known as the wassail bowl of Christmas time and the New Year. In the Middle Ages, St. Bartholomew was the patron saint of the honey crop and mead festivals were traditionally held on St. Bartholomew's Day, August 24. Mead was for thousands of years the only alcoholic drink known to man, but the discovery of fermentable grapes to make wine and of malted grains to make beer began the demise of mead. In the early 18th century, inexpensive sugar replaced honey as the primary sweetener. Mead, once the drink of kings, is now a rarity produced mainly for home use by beekeepers and home brewers.

An adult may make 100 gallons of mead per year. Households with 2 adults may make 200 gallons. It is illegal to sell mead without a special license.

The American Mead Association is an organization of mead enthusiasts headed by Susanne Price. Contact her for more information at the following address.

The American Mead Association
Post Office Box 17511
Boulder, Colorado 80308

Recommended Reading
The Art of Making Wine
by Stanley Anderson with Raymond Hull
and
Progressive Winemaking
by Peter Duncan and Bryan Acton

EQUIPMENT AND SUPPLIES

Request a few wine-making supply catalogs (see Appendix A). The drawings and descriptions explain the equipment and ingredients. All equipment and supplies (even bottles) are sold by mail. The equipment used to make mead is the same as that used to make beer (see page 9) and wine. Each formula makes 5 gallons. To make 1 gallon, divide the ingredients by 5, except for the yeast. One package of yeast is used for 1 to 5 gallons of mead.

- ❑ 2 five-gallon glass carboys
- ❑ 6.7-gallon plastic fermentation bucket with cover and air lock
- ❑ 6 feet of 3/8-inch clear plastic hose
- ❑ 2 air locks (Drawing on page 55.)
- ❑ 2 carboy stoppers drilled with holes to fit the air locks
- ❑ Floating thermometer (32 to 212 degrees F.)
- ❑ Triple-scale hydrometer (.990 to 1.120 specific gravity)
- ❑ Bottles, caps and capper
- ❑ 3-to-4-gallon enamel or stainless steel pot

GENERAL DIRECTIONS

Step 1: (Day 1) Sanitize
Sanitize everything that touches mead with one of the following solutions. Save the solution as it may be used repeatedly (until the smell is gone).

Sanitizing Solution I

8 crushed campden tablets
1 teaspoon acid blend
2 cups water

Crush the campden tablets in a little water and combine all the ingredients. Rinse equipment in this solution, then rinse in hot tap water.

Sanitizing Solution II

2 tablespoons chlorine laundry bleach

1 gallon water

Mix the ingredients. Soak equipment 15 minutes in the solution. Rinse everything well in hot tap water.

Caution: Do not mix other cleaning agents with chlorine bleach

Step 2: (Day 1) In a bucket, mix about 3/4 of the honey with two gallons warm water. Add cold water to equal 5 gallons and stir for 5 to 10 minutes until it is well mixed. Take a specific gravity reading with a hydrometer. A hydrometer is as easy to use as a thermometer and instructions come with it. The specific gravity indicates how much sugar (honey) is in a solution and how much alcohol will be produced. Wine should contain at least 10% alcohol.

Beginning Specific Gravity	Potential Alcohol by %
1.080	10.6
1.085	11.3
1.090	12.0
1.095	12.7
1.100	13.4
1.105	14.1
1.110	14.9

Add more honey to increase the reading or add more water to decrease the reading. When the specific gravity is adjusted and the total volume is 5 gallons, add the remaining ingredients *except for the yeast and campden tablets*. Mix well. This mixture is called *must*. Remove two cups of the must and set it aside. Crush 10 campden tablets in a little water. Add this to the bucket of must and mix well. Cover the bucket with an airtight lid and allow it to stand for 24 hours. Make a yeast starter. To do this, boil the 2 cups of reserved must and let it cool to 110 degrees F. Add the yeast, wait 10 minutes, and stir well. Cover the mixture with a clean cloth and allow it to set in a dark, warm (75 to 80 degrees F.) place for 24 hours. Foaming indicates the yeast is active. If there is no foam, try another packet of yeast.

Step 3: (Day 2 or 24 hours later)
Sanitize all equipment. Add the yeast starter to the must. Stir to mix well. Divide the must between one carboy and the bucket. Each should be only half full to allow for foaming. Cover the bucket and attach a fermentation lock. Fit the carboy with a rubber stopper and air lock.

Fermentation or air locks are designed to allow carbon dioxide to escape the fermenting must, yet it keeps airborne yeast and bacteria from entering. It must always be half-filled with vodka. Allow the must to ferment in a dark place at a stable temperature (75 to 80 degrees F.) until violent foaming begins (1 to 3 days). Carbon dioxide should be rapidly bubbling from the air lock.

Step 4: Move the must to a cooler place (60 to 70 degrees F.) and ferment until the air lock shows only one bubble per minute (14 to 28 days). The specific gravity will be near 1.020 to 1.040.

Step 5: Sanitize a hose and carboy. Siphon the must from the carboy and bucket into the clean carboy, leaving sediment behind. Introduce as little oxygen as possible by keeping both ends of the siphoning hose underneath the wine surface. Fill the carboy within 1 inch of the top with boiled water that has been allowed to cool. Insert a drilled rubber stopper and an air lock half-filled with vodka. Allow this to ferment in a dark place at a stable temperature (60 to 70 degrees F.) until no bubbles are escaping the air lock and another deposit has settled (2 to 6 weeks).

Siphoning finished mead.

Step 6: Racking
Sanitize a hose and carboy. Crush 5 campden tablets in a tablespoon of water. Add the campden tablets to the clean carboy. Siphon into the clean carboy and leave the sediment behind. Introduce as little oxygen as possible. Keep the end of the siphoning hose underneath the wine surface. Fill the carboy within 1 inch of the top with boiled water that has been cooled. Insert a sanitized air lock half-filled with vodka. Maintain 65 to 68 degrees F. until another deposit has settled (about 3 months).

Step 7: Repeat Step 6 until there is no bubbling through the air lock, the mead is clear and there is no sediment. Fill the carboy to within 1 inch of the top each time it is racked. Ending specific gravity should be between .990 and 1.008. (1 to 4 rackings, 3 months between each racking).

At this point choose to make a finished mead or a sparkling mead. The mead along with 1 campden tablet may be siphoned into gallon jugs at the last racking. If making vinegar or sparkling mead, do not add campden tablets at the last racking.

FINISHING MEAD

Adjusting Sweetness

Mead Type	Beginning Gravity	Ending Gravity
Sparkling wine	1.070	.990 to 1.000
Dry table wine	1.090	.990 to 1.000
Medium social wine	1.110	1.000 to 1.008
Sweet dessert wine	1.110	1.008 & above
Not advisable	Over 1.110	Over 1.035

Dry mead can be sweetened to the desired ending gravity before bottling. To sweeten 1 gallon of mead, add 1/2 teaspoon stabilizer (such as potassium sorbate) and 1 dissolved campden tablet. Wait 24 hours. Make small additions of sugar (about 1 tablespoon) until the sweetness suits your taste or the ending specific gravity desired. Do not use honey because it creates sediment. Two ounces of sugar will raise one gallon of wine by .005. Be sure to stir well between each addition of sugar and before measuring the specific gravity. When the sweetness is agreeable, bottle the mead.

Bottling and Aging Mead:
Bottle mead 3 months after a racking. Crush 1/2 campden tablet per gallon of mead and place it in a sanitized container. Siphon the mead into the container and mix it with the campden tablets without introducing oxygen. Bottle mead in sanitized, flint (clear), burgundy-style bottles. Soak corks 5 minutes in a sanitizing solution. Rinse them well in hot tap water. Bottle and cork the wine leaving a 3/4-inch head space beneath the cork. Corks should be recessed about 1/16 inch below the neck of the bottle. Leave the bottles upright for 2 days and then always store them on their sides to keep the corks wet. Age mead in a cool, dark place (55 degrees F. is ideal). Sweet wines and wines with a low alcohol and tannin content are drinkable sooner than other wines.

SPARKLING MEAD

Any wine of the mead family can be made into sparkling mead if potassium sorbate and campden tablets are not added at the last racking. Ideally, sparkling mead contains 10% alcohol and 6.9 p.p.t. tartaric acid. The following is a good formula.

Approximately 10 pounds honey or a specific gravity of 1.070
5 teaspoons yeast nutrient or energizer
3 cups orange juice
4 ounces (weight) tartaric acid
1 ounce (weight) tannin
Champagne yeast

Step 1: Follow the mead General Directions. Crown caps for soft drinks also fit domestic champagne bottles. Use sanitized champagne bottles that can withstand carbonation pressure. Dissolve 1 package of champagne yeast in 1/2 cup 110 degree F. water. Let it stand for 10 minutes. Foaming indicates the yeast is active. If there is no foam, try another package of yeast.

Step 2: Add 2 level teaspoons sugar and 10 drops of the yeast solution to each champagne bottle. Do not use honey as its sugar content varies. Fill the bottles within 2 inches of the top. Insert champagne stoppers or attach crown caps. Tilt the bottles to dissolve the sugar. Store the bottles upright at 70 degrees for one week.

Step 3: Store the bottles upright in a dark place between 50 and 70 degrees F. for 6 months.

Step 4: Keep the sparkling mead upright and chill it. Pour the mead at eye level, watching the sediment. Pour the second glass without turning the bottle upright. Cease pouring when the sediment reaches the neck. Books about sparkling wine, such as ***How to Make Wines With a Sparkle*** by J. Restall and D. Hebbs, describe methods of removing the yeast deposit before the mead is served.

CYSER

Mead from honey and apple juice is called *cyser,* from which the word cider is derived. It is believed to be the "strong drink" referred to in the Bible.

5 gallons apple juice (no preservatives)
6 pounds honey
5 teaspoons acid blend
1 1/4 teaspoons tannin
3 teaspoons pectic enzyme (or as the product directs)
5 teaspoons energizer
Champagne yeast

MEAD

♦ **Dry mead,** suitable as a dinner wine, is made from 10 to 15 pounds honey or a beginning specific gravity between 1.085 and 1.095. Use 3 teaspoons acid blend to ferment dry mead.

♦ **Sweet mead**, suitable for social drinking or as a dessert wine, is made from 15 to 17 pounds honey or a beginning specific gravity no higher than 1.110. High specific gravities can stop fermentation prematurely. If a very sweet mead is desired, sweeten it as described in "Adjusting Sweetness" on page 56. Use 4 teaspoons acid blend in sweet mead.

To Dry or Sweet Mead Add:
1/8 teaspoon tannin
5 teaspoons yeast nutrient or energizer
Champagne yeast

MEAD EXTRACT

See page 47.

MELOMEL

Melomel is mead from vegetable or fruit juices other than apple or grape. Melomels were fashionable during the Middle Ages.

Berry Melomel
Use ONE of the following fresh or frozen berries:
20 pounds blackberries
12 1/2 pounds blueberries
15 pounds raspberries
17 1/2 pounds strawberries
Add:
10 pounds honey
1/4 teaspoon tannin
6 1/4 teaspoons acid blend
5 teaspoons pectic enzyme (or as the product directs)
5 teaspoons yeast nutrient or energizer
Champagne yeast

Wash and drain the fruit. Put it into a nylon straining bag or panty hose. Crush the fruit, strain the juice into a bucket and keep the pulp in the bag. Tie the top of the bag and add it to the bucket.

Follow the General Directions for mead, omitting the beginning specific gravity reading. The sugar in the fruit has not been released and it will not register on the hydrometer. Stir the must 4 times daily and squeeze the bag to help extract juices. Remove the bag after 5 or 6 days. Continue with Step 4 of the General Directions.

Melomels from Fruit Concentrates: Wine-making suppliers sell canned fruit concentrates in many flavors: apricot, blackberry, blueberry, cherry, cranberry, gooseberry, loganberry, peach, plum, raspberry and strawberry. Replace the sugar requested in the concentrate recipes with honey.

METHEGLYN AND HIPPOCRAS

Metheglyn is spiced mead. Hippocras is named for the physician, Hippocrates, who preserved medicinal herbs in pyment (page 59) for administration to the sick. Boil the flavoring agent in water to extract the flavor. Use the cooled, flavored water as part of the must. Ground spices added after fermentation cloud mead. It is difficult to clear. Liqueur spice combinations are appropriate for Hippocras and Metheglyn. See page 49 for liqueurs.

Christmas Spice
At bottling time, into each 750 ml bottle place:
1 whole clove
A tiny sliver of whole nutmeg
1/4 inch piece cinnamon stick

PYMENT

Mead from honey and grapes is called pyment. Pyment originated in the Bordeaux region of France and was very popular throughout the Middle Ages, especially in 14th century England.

10 pounds light raisins
7 1/2 pounds honey
5 tablespoons acid blend
2 1/2 teaspoons pectic enzyme (or as the product directs)
1 teaspoon tannin
2 1/2 teaspoons yeast nutrient or energizer
Champagne yeast

Add enough hot water to grind the raisins in a food processor. Follow the instructions listed under "Berry Melomel" on page 58.

Pyment from Concentrates:
Wine-making suppliers sell white and red grape concentrates. Replace the sugar requested in the recipe with honey.

MEAD VINEGAR

See page 97.

MEASURING BEESWAX

Usually there is a great difference between the liquid volume of an ingredient and its dry weight. This is not true of beeswax. Example: 1 ounce weight of solid beeswax is equal to 1 ounce liquid measurement of melted wax. The following chart can be used to measure beeswax as a solid or a liquid.

Melted Beeswax or Liquid Measure	Equals Solid Wax or Dry Weight
1 tablespoon	1/2 ounce
2 tablespoons or 1 ounce	1 ounce
1/4 cup or 4 tablespoons	2 ounces
1/2 cup or 8 tablespoons	4 ounces or 1/4 pound
1 cup or 16 tablespoons	8 ounces or 1/2 pound
2 cups or 16 ounces	1 pound or 16 ounces

LIQUID DISPLACEMENT

Solid beeswax can be measured by displacing liquid. For example, to measure 1 tablespoon beeswax use the following method.

Since four tablespoons of liquid equal 1/4 cup, add 3 tablespoons of water to a clear measuring cup. Add lumps of solid wax until the water reaches the 1/4 cup line. Pour off the water. The remaining wax equals 1 tablespoon.

Set the wax aside to dry before using it in any formula.

MEAT

"The Sausage Maker" (see Appendix A) sells Prague Powder and corn syrup solids. They also sell Rytek Kutas' book, ***Great Sausage Recipes and Meat Curing.*** This book is appropriately named. It contains these two formulas plus 500 pages of information about curing meat and making sausage. Customers may use the free advice line: (716) 876-5521.

WARNING: The Prague Powder ingredient in these formulas is sodium nitrate in a salt carrier. This meat cure is vital to prevent botulism.

HONEY-CURED BACON

1 pound salt
2 tablespoons plus 2 teaspoons Prague Powder Number One
3 cups honey

From a butcher, obtain a fresh slab of bacon that has been properly squared. Mix the salt and Prague Powder and thoroughly rub it into the bacon. Pour the honey onto the bacon and rub it in evenly. Wrap the bacon in plastic-lined freezer wrap and place it in a 38 degree F. cooler for 6 days.

Remove the bacon from the cooler and wash it beneath running water. Rub the bacon to help remove the salt cure and honey. Do not allow it to soak in the water. Hang the bacon to dry at room temperature for 30 minutes.

Smoking: With dampers fully open, smoke the bacon in a preheated 135 degree F. smoker until the bacon is dry. Close the dampers to 1/4 open and apply hickory smoke until the internal temperature reaches 128 degrees F. Reduce the temperature to 120 degrees F. and hold until the desired color is obtained. Remove the bacon and place it in a cooler overnight before slicing it.

Note: "The Sausage Maker" also sells dry cures to make honey-cured bacon or ham. Complete instructions come with each product.

HONEY LOAF

5 pounds pork butt
1 cup ice water
2 ounces (weight) salt
1 3/4 ounce corn syrup solids
4 ounces (weight) honey
2 teaspoons onion powder
1 1/2 teaspoon ground white pepper
1 teaspoon ground celery seed
1 teaspoon Prague Powder Number One

Grind the lean meat through a coarse plate (about 3/8-inch). Grind the fat meat through a fine plate (3/16-inch or smaller). Mix the Prague Powder with the water and then mix all ingredients. Form a loaf and place it in a deep pan such as a Dutch oven.

Add 1 cup water and cover the pan. Bake at 160 degrees F. until the internal temperature of the loaf reaches 152 degrees F. Add more water as it evaporates. Remove the loaf and chill it in ice water until the internal temperature falls to 70 degrees F. Place the loaf in the refrigerator for 24 hours before slicing it. This is a good sandwich meat. Honey Loaf may also be stuffed into a fibrous casing about 5 to 6 inches in diameter. Casings are also sold by "The Sausage Maker".

METAL

The ingredients for this section are available from laboratory suppliers such as "Hagenow Laboratories" and "Chem Lab" (see Appendix A). See page 71 for metal-polishing cloths.

ALUMINUM POLISH

Parts by weight:
1 part beeswax
3 parts mineral oil
4 parts magnesium oxide powder, pure
3 parts calcium carbonate powder, pure
2 parts iron oxide (ferric) red powder

Melt the beeswax and mineral oil together. Stir in the remaining ingredients. Continue stirring until the mixture cools.

Apply the polish with a clean damp cloth. Rinse the aluminum and wipe it dry with a clean cloth.

BRASS CLEANER

Parts by weight:
2.4 parts beeswax
9.4 parts mineral oil
42 parts oxalic acid crystals, pure
42 parts Tripoli powder
42 parts liquid soap

Melt the beeswax and oil together in a microwave or a double boiler. Stir in the liquid soap. Add the Tripoli powder and acid crystals. Let the cleaner set overnight before using it.

Apply the polish with a clean, damp cloth. Rinse the brass and dry it with a clean cloth.

CHROME POLISH

Parts by weight:
1 part beeswax
3 parts mineral oil
1 part chromium oxide, green powder
1 part aluminum oxide powder

Melt the beeswax and oil together. Stir in the remaining ingredients and continue stirring until the mixture cools.

Apply the polish with a clean, damp cloth. Rinse the chrome and dry it with a clean cloth.

COPPER CLEANER

Parts by weight:
2.4 parts beeswax
9.4 parts mineral oil
42 parts vinegar, 5% to 7% acetic acid
42 parts citric acid, USP crystals
42 parts soap flakes

Combine the soap and vinegar to make a paste. Melt the beeswax and mineral oil together in a microwave or a double boiler. Stir in the soap mixture and citric acid. Let the cleaner set overnight before using it.

Apply the polish with a clean, damp cloth. Rinse the copper and wipe it dry with a clean cloth.

KNIFE-POLISHING STONE

Parts by weight:
3 parts beeswax
6 parts 4F pumice
1 part chrome oxide

continued

Melt the wax in a microwave or a double boiler. Stir in the pumice and oxide. Stir until the mixture sets and pour it into molds. Pumice is sold by "Woodworker's Supply" (see Appendix A) and other wood-finishing suppliers.

GREASELESS LUBRICATING PENCIL

Parts by weight:
1 part beeswax
1 part powdered graphite

Melt the beeswax in a microwave or a double boiler. Grind the graphite into a small amount of the melted wax. Combine the ingredients and pour into molds.

LUBRICATING STICK

Parts by weight:
53 parts wax
5 parts castor oil
33 parts powdered graphite
9 parts lampblack

Grind the dry ingredients in a small amount of the oil. Melt the wax and remaining oil in a microwave or a double boiler. Combine all ingredients and pour into small molds or paper tubes.

MEASURING TAPES

Add new snap to a metal measuring tape by polishing it with paste or liquid beeswax polish (page 79).

RUST PREVENTATIVE

2 ounces (weight) beeswax
2 cups turpentine
2 tablespoons linseed oil

Melt the beeswax in a microwave. Stir the wax into the turpentine and add the linseed oil.

Dip clean metal into the mixture and set it aside to dry. This is good for tools, shovels and nails. To treat nails, dip them into the mixture and scatter them to dry.

SAW BLADES

Draw a block of beeswax over saw blades to keep them from binding.

SILVER POLISH

This polish is also good for chrome, stainless steel and porcelain.

Parts by weight:
2 parts beeswax
12 parts mineral oil
9 parts magnesium carbonate
3 parts powdered calcium carbonate

Melt the beeswax and mineral oil in a microwave or a double boiler. Stir in the dry ingredients and continue stirring until the mixture cools.

Apply the polish with a clean damp cloth. Rinse the item and dry it with a clean cloth.

SNOW SHOVELS

Wax snow shovels to make the snow slide off easily. (See "Polish", page 79.)

SOLE PLATES

Apply wax or polish to the sole plates of electric tools to make them slide easily.

MIRROR ART

The front of mirrors can be etched as described in "Etching Glass" (see page 30) to leave a frosted appearance on the front of mirrors. The backs of mirrors are covered in silver and protective coatings. Stained glass suppliers (see Appendix A) sell "Strip Silver 1" designed to remove mirror backing. "Strip Silver 2" is designed to remove silver from mirrors and leaves clear glass with no frosted appearance. Paint, colored foil, fabric or photographs can be placed behind the mirror to show through the clear sections.

GENERAL DIRECTIONS

Step 1: Place a can in a dry electric skillet set at 300 degrees F. Place beeswax in the can to melt.

Step 2: Mirrors are backed by several different coatings. This removal process works best on mirrors that are backed with gray or black coatings. Spray "Strip Silver 1" over the entire back of the mirror, or use ordinary paint remover (page 74). Apply the remover to the backing and wait until the backing crumples and bubbles. It is then easily peeled back and removed with a paper towel. Some mirrors may require a second coat. Once the backing is removed, be careful not to scratch the silver coating that remains. Gently clean the back of the mirror with window cleaner and wipe it dry with a paper towel.

Step 3: Lightly trace designs onto the silver backing with carbon paper. Remember to trace letters and numbers so they will face in the right direction when viewed from the *front.* See page 6 for ways to apply wax. Apply wax on the back of the mirror over the silver areas to be protected. These waxed areas will retain the mirror appearance when viewed from the front. Masking or electrical tape can be used to make straight lines or to cover large areas. Be sure the tape is pressed firmly at the corners.

Step 4: Apply "Strip Silver 2" with a soft brush over the unwaxed areas. "Strip Silver 2" dissolves the silver immediately upon contact. When all the unwaxed areas are stripped, clean the mirror with window cleaner and wipe it dry with a paper towel.

Step 5: Place the mirror over a pot of water and heat it until melted wax can be wiped away. Run the mirror through a dishwasher cycle to remove the last trace of wax.

MOCK MARBLE

Items cast in this mixture simulate marble. Glue is added to the plaster to harden it. Color streaks are added, the form is saturated with wax and polished with a soft cloth.

1 tablespoon water-soluble white glue
(such as Elmer's ® Glue-All)
1/2 cup water
1 1/2 cups plaster of Paris
Beeswax

Mix the glue and water. Add the plaster of Paris. Wait 5 minutes and stir the mixture until it is thick. Pour poster paint over the surface of the plaster or sprinkle dry artist's pigments over the surface. Cut through the plaster with a knife to make streaks of color. Do not stir. Pour the plaster into a mold and let it harden (1 to 2 hours). Remove the molded figure and wait for it to dry completely. Place the figure and enough wax to cover it in a 200 degree F. oven for 1 hour. Remove the figure, wait for it to cool, and polish it with a damp cloth.

MODELING WAX

Candle appliqué from modeling wax.

Modeling wax offers tremendous crafting possibilities. Modeling wax is extremely pliant and adherent when warmed, and it becomes hard again when cool. It is an ideal wax for hand-formed candles. When heated, its adhesive characteristics make it suitable to dribble down candles or bottles for special effects. Modeling wax can be molded to make candle wraps and appliqué.

GENERAL DIRECTIONS

Ingredients are sold by candle-making suppliers (see Appendix A). Paraffin wax is sold by numbers representing the melting point. Note that household paraffin sold in grocery stores has a melting point of only 120 degrees F. Use coloring designed for candles to color the wax. If the wax is molded in a large chunk, the color can be judged from the melted wax. If it is poured or otherwise made into thin sheets, the melted wax should be colored darker. Thin sheets of modeling wax are slightly transparent and the color appears lighter. Modeling wax with no coloring or scent added can be used for "Lost Wax Investment Casting" (page 49).

Alcohol Burners: Wax may be stuck into place by melting the wax over an alcohol burner. Other flames may produce carbon marks on the wax. Alcohol burners are inexpensive and sold by "Chem Lab" and "Hagenow Laboratories" (see Appendix A). A glass jar with a metal lid can be made into an alcohol burner. Drill a 1/4-to-3/8-inch hole in the metal lid. Thread a large wick through the hole. Wicks sold for oil lamps are suitable. As fuel, use only denatured alcohol (sometimes labeled "denatured solvent") sold with paint supplies. The colorless part of the flame (in the middle) is hottest. Electric pens such as those used for wood burning may also be used to melt wax. "Sticky Wax" (see page 13) can be used to connect pieces of modeling wax.

MODELING WAX I

1/2 pound 129/132 paraffin wax
1 pound beeswax

MODELING WAX II

2 pounds beeswax
3 ounces (weight) petroleum jelly

MODELING WAX III

1 pound beeswax
1 pound micro crystalline wax
(M-205 from "Barker Enterprises". See Appendix A)

MODELING WAX SHEETS

Place the waxes in a heat-proof container and melt them in a 200 degree F. oven. Cool the wax to 170 degrees F. and pour it onto a clean, smooth surface. A non-stick cookie sheet works well. Other surfaces should be sprayed with a wax-release agent.

Water can be placed in the pan and wax poured over it. This creates interesting lines and texture in the wax. It is possible to pour several colors at once to create marbled sheets of wax.

Pour the wax about 1/8 inch thick. A 12-by-18-inch cookie sheet holds between 3/4 and 1 pound of wax. Do not move the sheet while the wax is cooling. When the wax is hard, but still warm, pull it from the container. The wax may be used immediately or broken into pieces and warmed again when needed. Cut designs from wax sheets while the wax is warm and pliable. To keep wax at a workable temperature, use an electric hot pad, skillet or griddle. Use the lowest heat setting and cover the electric appliance with 2 or 3 thicknesses of cloth. Place the wax sheet on the cloth and be alert in case the temperature gets too warm. If the warm wax is still too brittle or difficult to knead, melt it and add a little oil, petroleum jelly or lanolin.

Books about silk and paper flowers usually contain patterns that can be used to make wax flowers. Sheets of wax can be rolled to form candles (see page 14 for rolled candles). Sheets of wax can be loosely rolled and cooled. Thin pieces of wax are easily broken off as they are needed and softened in warm water.

MOLDING MODELING WAX

Modeling wax can be molded, but it has poor release characteristics. The use of rubber molds and wax-release agents overcomes this drawback.

CANDLE WRAPS AND APPLIQUÉ

"Pourette" and "Deep Flex" (see Appendix A) sell many molds for wax appliqué. Pour the wax at 165 degrees F. The thinner the appliqué, the easier it is to apply it to the candle. Wait until the wax hardens, yet is still slightly warm. Remove the appliqué from the mold. Coat the back with rubber cement. Begin at one edge of the appliqué and gently press it against the contour of the candle. If the modeling wax cracks, it was probably too hot. If it breaks cleanly, it was too cold. See page 15 for "Craft Wax Appliqué".

MODELING AND SCULPTING

Modeling wax can be poured into a large container and allowed to cool. Use a knife or saw to cut workable pieces from the wax or soften the large block of wax in hot water. The wax can be shaped by hand or with carving and sculpture tools.

It may be helpful to dip the tools or fingers into water to keep the wax from being too sticky. Glycerin is also a good lubricant. Clean the tools often on a cloth dampened with naphtha (cigarette lighter fluid), turpentine or mineral spirits.

MOLDS OF PLASTER

Plaster of Paris and rubber molds.

Plaster of Paris is sold in craft stores and paint supply stores. It can be used to make molds from models made of wax, metal, clay, plaster, wood, plastic or glass.

Choosing Models: The inflexibility of plaster means that the model must be relatively smooth and free of undercuts and that the mold must have two or more sections.

An undercut is a sharp angle, hook or an area deeper than the surrounding surface that locks the plaster onto the model. Holes such as the one created by the bear's arm (see the photograph) must be filled with clay or modeling wax to insure release of the mold.

Once the model is chosen, choose a container large enough to contain the model and plaster. Waxed milk cartons are good containers as they require no lubrication. Other containers must be lubricated. The container must be large enough to allow 1 inch of plaster around the model.

Lubrication: Petroleum jelly (page 77), thinned to a watery consistency with mineral spirits, is an excellent mold release agent. Mineral oil, silicone wax-release agents, and beeswax polishes (see page 79) also work well as lubricants.

Plaster Mixture: Pour 1 measure of water into a clean container. Sift 2 measures of plaster of Paris powder through the fingers into the water. Let this sit without stirring for 5 minutes, then mix it to a thick, soupy consistency. Stir for about a minute, incorporating as few bubbles as possible.

GENERAL DIRECTIONS

Step 1: Pour about 1/4 of the plaster required and tap the container on the tabletop to release bubbles. Pour the next quarter and tap it again. Wait until the plaster is nearly setting, but still soft (10 to 15 minutes). It must be firm enough to support the model and keep it from sinking to the bottom.

Step 2: Lubricate the model and press it halfway into the plaster. The bottom of the model should be flush with the side of the carton to create a pour opening. Press a couple of lubricated marbles less than halfway into the plaster. The marbles create "keys" to help align the mold when it is put together. Remove the marbles after 30 minutes or when the plaster is at its warmest temperature. Wait 1 hour from pouring for the plaster to harden and cool.

Step 3: Lubricate the exposed model and plaster. Mix and pour enough plaster to cover the model. Wait 1 hour for the plaster to harden or until the plaster becomes quite warm. Tear away the carton, carefully pry apart the plaster halves and remove the model.

Step 4: The soft, fragile mold can be lubricated and used immediately to mold wax or it can be held together with rubber bands and allowed to dry and harden. It takes about a week for the mold to dry. Once it is dry it must be lubricated and soaked in water before molding wax. Soak the plaster in cold water until bubbles stop rising (about 5 minutes). Remove the mold and dry it with a towel. Remove water droplets in concave areas with a dry artist's brush. Fasten the mold halves together with rubber bands and pour the wax between 170 and 190 degrees F. Allow the wax to harden. To make a wax shell, allow the wax to harden until it is between 1/6 and 1/4 inch thick, and pour out the melted wax.

Plaster Molds in Relief: To copy three sides of a thin, flat object, glue it to a flat surface with rubber cement, silicone or bathtub chalk. Allow this to dry. Lubricate the model and pour plaster of Paris over it. Wait 1 hour for the plaster to harden. Run a knife or spatula underneath the plaster to lift it. Remove the model.

MOLDS OF LIQUID RUBBER LATEX

Candle-making suppliers and "Earth Guild" (see Appendix A) sell liquid latex rubber. This liquid is often painted over the backs of rugs to keep them from slipping. It may be used over models made of wax, metal, clay, plaster, wood, plastic or glass to make molds. Liquid latex is cold curing, and when dried it becomes firm, elastic and water-repellent.

Choosing Models: Follow the directions under "Molds of Plaster" (page 66) for choosing a model and choose models with the thought of pulling off the latex mold. Latex is flexible and can be turned inside out. It is more forgiving of undercuts in the model than plaster, but models with holes or severe undercuts will lock the latex onto the model and they cannot be separated. If the latex is difficult to remove, a tiny slit may be made halfway up one side, or both. If no lubricant is applied to the latex, the slit can be held together with tape.

GENERAL DIRECTIONS

Step 1: Mount the model on a level work surface with rubber cement, silicone or bath tub chalk and allow it to dry. Brush a thin coat of latex rubber over the model. Pop any bubbles and avoid a buildup in crevices that will require extra drying time.

Step 2: Make a flange by forming a 2-inch base around the model (see the drawing below). The flange supports the mold during casting. Store the brush in house-hold ammonia between latex applications. Allow the latex rubber to dry completely until all traces of white are gone and the coating appears a translucent-tan color.

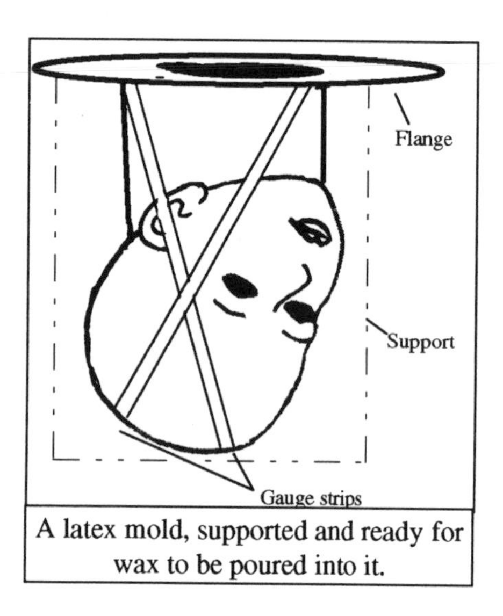

A latex mold, supported and ready for wax to be poured into it.

Step 3: Continue applying thin coats and allowing them to dry. Subsequent coats may be applied thicker. If the mold is too thin, it will stretch and distortion may occur. If it is made too thick, it is difficult to remove without cutting it. A 3-inch model will require 6 to 8 coats and larger models, 8 to 10 coats. Reinforce large molds with strips of cloth or gauze bandage applied vertically in the wet latex (see the drawing). These strips keep the mold from stretching when it is later supported by its flange. Allow the model to set for 24 hours after the last coat.

Step 4: Dust latex rubber with talc or lubricate it with hand cream to keep it from sticking to itself when it is peeled from the model. Strengthen the mold by boiling it in water for 20 minutes. This heat-curing preserves the shape and imparts longer life to the mold.

Step 5: Suspend the dry mold by its flange on a level surface. A hole cut in a cardboard box works well. Fill the mold with casting medium (wax, plaster or resin) and allow it to harden. Peel off the mold. Casting resins are sold by "Deep Flex" (see Appendix A).

Latex Molds in Relief: Relief molds are three sides of a thin, flat object such as a coin. Glue the object to a flat surface with silicone glue or rubber cement and let it dry. Paint the object with liquid latex rubber and allow it to dry. Apply 2 or 3 additional coats, allowing each to dry before the next is applied. Reinforce the thin latex mold by pouring plaster of Paris over it. Allow at least one hour for the plaster to set. Run a knife or spatula under the mold to lift it and remove the model.

MOLDS OF SAND

Wax, concrete, and plaster of Paris can be molded in wet sand. Sand gives a granular appearance to the molded item and this texture is attractive on certain items.

Step 1: Use ordinary builder's sand that is very wet, but not runny. The drier the sand, the more sand will stick to the beeswax. Place the sand in a container large enough to hold the model.

Step 2: Firmly press the sand into the container and level the surface. The model does not require lubrication. Press it into the sand. Instead of using a model, the sand can be hand formed into designs.

Step 3: Remove the model and check the imprint to be sure that it is clear and that no loose sand has fallen into it.

Step 4: With the pouring spout close to the bottom of the impression, pour 170 degree F. melted beeswax. Allow the wax to cool and remove it from the mold.

Step 5: Wash the molded beeswax in hot running water to remove loose particles of sand.

MOLDS OF WAX

The impermeable surface of wax
makes it an ideal mold for plaster, cements
and resins.

Molds of wax
are finely detailed
and used mainly for relief work.

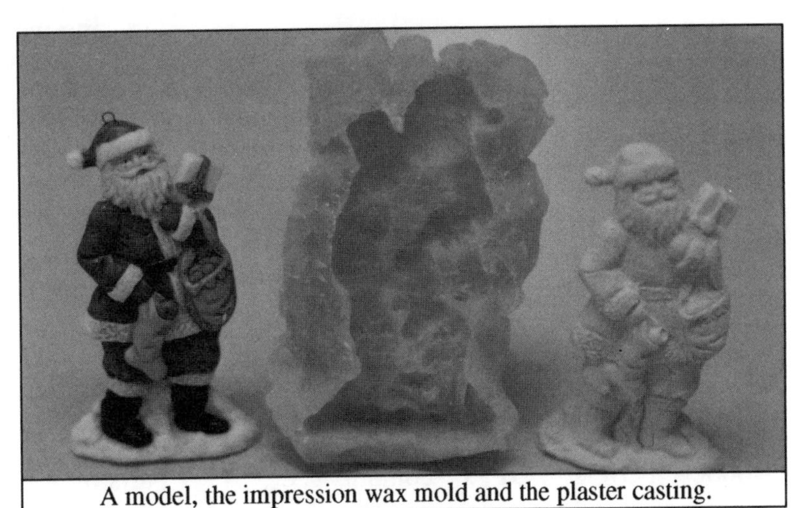

A model, the impression wax mold and the plaster casting.

IMPRESSION WAX

Parts by weight:
4 parts beeswax
1 part olive oil
4 parts dry laundry starch

Melt the ingredients to 170 degrees F. Cast the wax into sheets between 1/4 and 1/2-inch thick.

GENERAL DIRECTIONS

Step 1: Select a model with a hard, nonporous surface. Spray the model with a silicone wax-release agent.

Step 2: See page 64 for "Modeling Wax". The formulas there are also good impression waxes and directions for softening wax are given. Soften modeling wax or impression wax and firmly press the warm wax onto the model. Wait for the wax to cool and harden, or place it in a refrigerator to cool quickly.

Step 3: Remove the model and fill the impression with plaster, cement or resin. Allow 1 hour for plaster to harden and remove it from the wax mold. The soft plaster can be gently scraped to smooth imperfections. If the plaster breaks, super glue will bond it. Set the plaster aside to further dry and harden. Casting resins are sold by "Deep Flex" (see Appendix A).

OLD FORMULAS

The following formulas may be old, but they can still be useful. They could spark an idea for a new product.

AUTOMOBILE POLISH

The old-style formulation of automobile polish is the same as the polish formulas listed under "Polish" (see page 79).

BLUEPRINTS

In the 1800's, blueprints were made waterproof by dipping them into melted wax. The prints were placed between two cloths and ironed to remove excess wax. Often cheesecloth was melted onto the back of the paper to reinforce it.

BREWER'S PITCH

This is an odorless, waterproof seal for wooden barrels. It was once used inside wooden barrels used to contain beer, wine and vinegar.

Parts by weight:
55 parts rosin
43 parts paraffin
2 parts beeswax

Heat the ingredients at 250 degrees F. until they are combined. Heat the pitch with a torch to spread it over the inside of the wooden barrel.

CANARY PASTE

1 cup blanched almonds
1 cup cornmeal
2 tablespoons unsalted butter
Enough honey to form a paste

Grind the almonds, cornmeal and butter together. Add enough honey to the mixture to form a thick paste.

GRAFTING WAX

10 ounces (weight) rosin
2 ounces (weight) beeswax
1 ounce (weight) charcoal powder
1 tablespoon linseed oil

Grafting wax seals the union of plant tissue. Heat the beeswax and rosin at 250 degrees F. until they melt. Stir in the remaining ingredients.

Allow the wax to cool to a spreadable consistency and brush it onto the graft. Charcoal and rosin are sold by "Chem Lab".

HEMP ROPE GREASE

Parts by weight:
2 parts fat
3 parts linseed oil
2 parts wax
3 parts petroleum jelly
6 parts rosin
1 part graphite
5 parts boiled linseed oil

Heat the first 5 ingredients together until they are well blended. Rub the graphite into the boiled linseed oil. Combine all ingredients. Rub the warm mixture over hemp ropes.

HOOF GREASE

2 ounces (weight) beeswax
1 cup mineral oil

continued

Heat the ingredients until the wax melts. Stir until it cools. Apply the mixture with a stiff brush.

IRONING WAX

Rub a cake of wax over a hot iron, then press canvas or unbleached muslin. This wax finish gives a gloss and protects the cloth from dirt and water. While the iron is still hot, wipe it clean with a paper towel.

MASSAGE BALL

In 1897 this item was said to relieve headaches and arthritis pain. Today it could be used for general massage.

4 ounces (weight) beeswax
1 teaspoon essential oil of camphor, menthol or wintergreen

Melt the beeswax in a microwave or a double boiler. Remove wax from the heat and stir in the essential oil. Pour the mixture into a container. Stir the wax occasionally as it cools. When the wax is cool enough to handle, form it into a ball. The surface may be smooth or bumpy. To use the massage ball, hold it in the palm of the hand and gently roll it over the affected part. Apply as much pressure as desired until there is a sensation of warmth. Store the ball wrapped in foil.

NON-STICK COOKING OIL

Commercial bakers once sprayed this mixture over baking pans to insure release of baked items. Beeswax thickens the mixture. It will stay on the sides of pans and not run off.

Parts by weight:
3 parts beeswax
4 parts vegetable shortening
5 parts corn oil

Heat the ingredients in a double boiler until they are combined.

OPAQUE NOISE-DEADENER FOR WINDOWS

Parts by weight:
1 part wax
10 parts turpentine
1 part shellac
1 part Japan drier

Melt the wax and shellac over low heat. Remove the mixture from heat and stir in the turpentine and Japan drier. Coat the outside of clean windows with this mixture. While it is still wet, dab it with cotton batting. Ingredients are available where paint supplies are sold.

PATENT LEATHER DRESSING

1 tablespoon beeswax
3 tablespoons olive oil
2 tablespoons turpentine

Heat the oil and wax until the wax melts. Remove this from the heat and stir in the turpentine. Rub a small amount of the mixture over patent leather, then wipe with a clean cloth.

POLISHING CLOTHS

Polishing cloths are graded according to the coarseness of the powder they contain. Dry emery powder makes a coarse polishing cloth suitable for base metals and objects that require considerable scouring. Fine Tripoli powder makes a fine grade polishing cloth suitable for soft metals, such as gold or silver. These powders are sold by "Hagenow Laboratories" (see Appendix A). See page 61 for metal polishes.

1/4 teaspoon grated beeswax continued

1/4 cup mineral or baby oil
1 1/2 cup turpentine solvent

Heat the oil and wax until the wax melts. Remove this from heat and stir in the turpentine. Saturate a soft flannel cloth in the mixture and wring it out tightly. Spread the cloth and allow it to dry slightly. Sprinkle both sides of the cloth with polishing powder and thoroughly rub it into the cloth. Spread the cloth and wait for it to dry. Shake it to remove excess powder.

GLOSS LAUNDRY STARCH

1/3 cup water
2 tablespoons dry laundry starch
4 cups water
1/2 teaspoon beeswax

Mix a paste of the starch and 1/3 cup cold water. Combine all ingredients and boil for 15 minutes. Dip fabric into the warm solution. Wring out the excess starch and hang the fabric to dry. The fabric should be damp when it is ironed. If it is dry, sprinkle it with water, roll the fabric in a ball and let it set 4 to 6 hours.

STOVE POLISH

Parts by weight:
33 parts graphite powder
5 parts beeswax
2 parts lampblack

Melt the beeswax in a microwave or a double boiler. Stir in the remaining ingredients and pour into molds. Graphite and lampblack are sold by "Hagenow Laboratories" (see Appendix A).

THREAD AND CLOTH

Manufacturers once used beeswax in the brushing phase of finishing cloth and thread. The wax provided a smooth finish that was removed at the first washing, but it made items appear more attractive on store displays.

TOOTHACHE PELLETS

1 tablespoon beeswax
2 drops clove essential oil

Melt the wax over low heat and add the oil. When the mixture is cool enough to handle, shape it into small balls about half the size of your thumbnail. Store these in a small covered jar. Use the pellets over aching teeth. They are good to use when a filling has been lost.

WOOD DRESSING

This finish protects floors, porches and outside stairways that have not been painted and where paint is not desired.

2 ounces (weight) beeswax
1 quart linseed oil

Melt the beeswax and stir it into the oil. Apply the mixture with a brush. (See page 73 for "Exterior Wood Finish" and page 103 for "Wood Finishes".)

WOODEN BUCKET REPAIR

Ounces by weight:
1 1/2 ounces lard
1 ounce salt
8 ounces beeswax
1 ounce wood charcoal powder

Melt the ingredients. While it is still warm, apply it to cracks or leaks in a dry wooden bucket. Wood charcoal powder is sold by "Chem Lab" and "Hagenow Laboratories" (see Appendix A).

OUTDOOR FORMULAS

EXTERIOR WOOD FINISH

This finish was developed by the United States Forest Products Laboratory. It is a durable finish that preserves the character of natural wood. It protects redwood or Western red cedar for 3 to 5 years. This finish was designed for siding, but has been used satisfactorily on wood fences, lawn furniture and sun decks.

1 pound beeswax
2 ounces (weight) zinc stearate
1 gallon turpentine or mineral spirits
1/2 gallon Pentachlorophenol,
concentrate, 10:1
3 gallons boiled linseed oil

Pentachlorophenol (commonly called "penta"), boiled linseed oil, turpentine and mineral spirits are sold by paint stores, building suppliers and lumber-yards. Zinc Stearate is sold by drug stores or "Chem Lab" (see Appendix A).

Melt the beeswax and zinc stearate in an oven set at 200 degrees F. Oven temperatures vary greatly. It is wise to use an oven thermometer and check it often. Pour the turpentine or mineral spirits into a 5-gallon bucket. With vigorous stirring, add the wax mixture to the bucket. Work outdoors or in a well-ventilated room and far from sparks or flame. Cool the mixture to room temperature and add the penta concentrate and linseed oil.

Use a single application of the finish by brush or spay. On a smooth surface, a gallon should cover 400 to 500 square feet; on rough, 200 to 250 square feet. It may be used over other penetrating natural finishes. Varnish films must be removed before this finish is applied. The drying time is approximately 24 hours. (See page 72 for "Wood Dressing".)

FLY PAPER

Hang these sticky strips from ceilings or walls to catch and kill flies.

Parts by weight:
4 parts rosin, yellow lumps
1 part Canada balsam
2 parts castor oil
2 parts honey

Melt the ingredients in a double boiler. By dipping or brushing, coat strips of paper or fabric with the hot mixture. Hang the strips in bright areas out of direct sunlight. Ingredients are sold by "Hagenow Laboratories" (see Appendix A).

WAX CAULKING CORD

Press this waxed cord into place around windows, doors and foundations to seal cracks and stop air leaks. This cord may be removed and later reapplied. It won't dry out or damage wood, metal or paint.

Obtain a sufficient length of 100% cotton cord or rug yarn (match the color of the yarn to the color of the trim work). Judge the amount of melted wax necessary to saturate the cord. Add 1 tablespoon baby or mineral oil to each 4 ounces of wax used. Melt the oil and wax in an oven set at 200 degrees F. Add the cord and wait 10 minutes. Wear rubber gloves to protect the hands from melted wax. Run the cord through the fingers to remove excess wax and set it aside to cool. Wind the cord into a ball for easy handling and storage.

NAILS AND SCREWS

Rub nails and screws over beeswax to ease their entry into wood.

ROACH KILLER

2 cups borax
1/4 cup honey
1/4 cup chopped onion

Make a paste of the ingredients. Add more borax or honey to adjust the mixture to a clay-like consistency. Roll, cut or hand-form the paste into tiny balls or crumbs. Place the roach killer where roaches are a problem, but out of the reach of children and pets. The roaches will eat the mixture and go away to die.

SEPTIC TANK TONIC

This formula promotes bacterial action in septic tanks and sewage treatment systems.

1 1/4 cup honey
1 envelope dried yeast
4 cups warm water

Add the honey to the water and allow it to cool to 80 degrees F. Stir in the yeast and allow it to stand in a warm place overnight. Pour the mixture down the sink or toilet.

SLUG BAIT

2 teaspoons honey
1/2 teaspoon baker's yeast
2 cups warm water (115 degrees F.)

Mix the ingredients. Dig a shallow depression in the soil and set a container into the soil with the top edge flush with the soil surface. Pour the bait into the container. The slugs are attracted to the yeasty, fermenting mixture and drown when they fall in. Add more bait, as it evaporates. Also see page 101.

PAINT REMOVAL

The wax in paint remover holds the solvent to vertical surfaces and prevents evaporation. The following formulas are suitable for stripping wood, metal and masonry. They lift wax, latex paint, oil paint, varnish, lacquer, enamel, shellac and polyurethane finishes away like a skin. They are useful for carved figures that must be stripped.

INGREDIENTS AND PRECAUTIONS

Ingredients are available from wood-finishing suppliers such as "Woodworker's Supply" and from chemical suppliers, such as "Chem Lab" and "Hagenow Laboratories" (see Appendix A).

Danger: Avoid open flames, provide adequate ventilation and follow the directions carefully.

Store strippers in tightly sealed metal or glass containers away from excessive heat and out of the reach of children. These formulas should be used within six months of mixing them. Do not use these removers on linoleum, plastic, rubber, asphalt tile, fiberglass or other synthetics. Wear solvent-resistant gloves and protective eye wear. Do not use these formulas in small enclosed areas where vapors can concentrate, such as basements, bathrooms or closets. Whenever possible, use them outdoors, at temperatures between 65 and 85 degrees F. and away from strong breezes and hot sun. If slight dizziness, headache, nausea or eye-watering is experienced, leave the area immediately, ventilation is inadequate.

PAINT STRIPPER I

5 quarts pure benzene
2 1/2 pints acetone
1/2 pint carbon tetrachloride
2 ounces (weight) beeswax

Grate the beeswax into the benzene and let it stand until the wax dissolves. Add the remaining ingredients.

PAINT STRIPPER II

Parts by weight:
1 part beeswax
3 parts benzene
3 parts toluene
4 parts alcohol
5 parts acetone
4 parts ethylene dichloride
1 part ethyl acetate

Combine the benzene and ethylene dichloride. Grate or shred the beeswax and add it to the mixture. Put the mixture in a tightly sealed metal or glass container and let it stand until the beeswax dissolves (stir or shake it often). Add the remaining ingredients.

PAINT STRIPPER III

Parts by weight:
1 part beeswax
6 parts mineral spirits
5 parts acetone
4 parts pure benzene
3 parts carbon tetrachloride
2 parts xylene

Combine the benzene, carbon tetrachloride and xylene. Grate or shred the beeswax and add it to the mixture. Put the mixture in a tightly sealed container and let it stand until the beeswax dissolves (stir or shake it often). Add the remaining ingredients.

GENERAL DIRECTIONS

Step 1: Shake the container and open it slowly to relieve pressure. With a brush, flow a thick coat of remover over the surface. Brush one time in one direction, not back and forth. Leave the area and wait 30 minutes.

Step 2: Test the finish by scraping a small area. If there is bare wood the finish is ready for removal. If not, wait until the test is positive. Multiple coats of paint or stubborn finishes may require repeated applications. As long as the stripper is wet, it is working. When the test is positive, remove the loosened finish with a nonmetallic scraper. Gently scrape off the finish in the direction of the wood grain. A brush or pointed stick helps remove old finish in recesses. The remover can be washed off with coarse rags dipped in warm, soapy water. Note that water may raise wood grain, loosen veneer or dissolve glued joints.

Step 3: Wash off any remaining compound with paint thinner or turpentine. Allow the wood to dry and sand it before refinishing it. Spread used rags and paper outdoors and allow them to dry. Dispose of them in a metal container.

PAPER

CARBON PAPER

Parts by weight:
6 parts carnauba wax
1 part beeswax
8 parts mineral oil
4 parts lampblack

Grind the oil and lampblack together. Melt the waxes. Stir the oil mixture into the waxes. When the mixture is between 100 and 120 degrees F., spread it over thin paper and allow it to harden. Ingredients are sold by chemical suppliers such as "Hagenow Laboratories" (see Appendix A).

COLORED WAX CHIPS

Paper can be decorated with color by scraping bits of wax candle coloring onto the paper. Melt the wax with by holding an iron 1/4 to 1/2 inch above it. Do not slide the iron because it blends the colors to a dirty gray.

DESIGN TRANSFER PAPER

With a sharp-pointed crayon, draw a design or pattern on lightweight paper. The thinner and darker the line, the better the image will transfer.

Lay the design face down on cloth or paper and run a medium-hot iron over the back. The design will be transferred.

MAGIC WRITING PAD

When the sheet is lifted from the coated cardboard, the writing disappears.

Parts by weight:
4 parts beeswax
9 parts Canada balsam
4 parts coconut oil
3 1/2 parts kaolin (clay)
1 part lampblack
2 parts mineral oil

Melt the wax, balsam, and coconut oil. Grind the lampblack into the mineral oil. Combine the mixtures. Brush the mixture over cardboard and allow it to cool.

Cover the cardboard with waxed paper, thin plastic, or flexible vinyl. Write on the pad with a stylus or a ball-point pen that is out of ink. Lift the sheet to erase the writing. Ingredients are sold by chemical suppliers (see Appendix A) such as "Hagenow Laboratories" .

MOTH-PROOF PAPER

This is an old-fashioned formula, but the essential oils can easily be changed to make a floral-scented wrapping paper.

4 ounces (weight) beeswax
1/4 teaspoon lavender essential oil
1/4 teaspoon pennyroyal essential oil
1/4 teaspoon clove essential oil
1 ounce (weight) soap
1 quart water

Dissolve the soap in hot water. Add the beeswax and heat until it is melted. Stir in the oils. Spray, paint or dip the wrapping paper to saturate it with the hot solution and hang it to dry. Use a few sheets of tissue paper inside the paper to keep oil off the wrapped item.

PAPER CUTTING

The Chinese use wax in their traditional method of cutting intricate designs out of paper. Several layers of thin paper are laid on a slab of wax and cut with a knife. The wax provides an excellent cutting surface, it keeps the papers from slipping, and it can be melted again when the surface is excessively marred by cuts.

PRINTING TRANSFER PAPER

Copy pictures from newspapers and magazines by rubbing them.

2 tablespoons soap powder or soap shavings
1/4 cup hot water
1 tablespoon turpentine

Heat the soap and water until the soap dissolves. Remove the mixture from the heat and stir in the turpentine. Brush the solution over the picture to be transferred. Comic strips transfer especially well. Wait about 10 seconds for the solution to sink in. Place a piece of paper over the picture and rub the back of it with the rounded side of a spoon. The picture will transfer to the paper. The solution can be stored indefinitely. If it solidifies, liquefy it in hot water before using it again.

WATERPROOF PAPER

4 ounces (weight) beeswax
6 ounces (weight) alum
1 ounce (weight) soap
1 quart water
Fragrant essential oil (optional)

Combine the ingredients and boil them for 10 minutes. Be sure the beeswax is melted. Dip paper into the hot solution and hang it to dry. Alum is sold in the grocer's spice section.

WAXED PAPER OR FABRIC

An easy way to coat paper or fabric with wax is done in an electric skillet. Set the skillet thermostat at 250 degree F. Place paper or fabric in the skillet and rub over it with a block of beeswax. If too much wax is applied, remove it with a cloth or iron the waxed item between clean cloths.
Note: To shine the top of a wood-burning cook stove, rub the hot surface with crumpled-up waxed paper.

PETROLEUM JELLY

PETROLEUM JELLY

Petroleum jelly is easy to make and it is an ingredient of many other products. Naturalists preferring not to use petroleum products may substitute a natural oil, such as grapeseed oil, for the mineral oil to make an "un-petroleum" jelly.

1 ounce (weight) beeswax
1/2 cup baby or mineral oil

Melt the ingredients in a microwave or a double boiler. Remove the mixture from heat and stir until it cools.

CHAPPED-LIP BALM

Petroleum jelly is good for chapped lips, but this formula is even better.

1 tablespoon shredded beeswax
1 tablespoon petroleum jelly
1 teaspoon honey

continued

1 tablespoon lanolin
3 to 4 drops essential oil

Melt the wax, lanolin and petroleum jelly in a microwave. Add the honey and essential oil. Essential oil of peppermint, eucalyptus, wintergreen and camphor slightly numb painful lips. Stir the mixture until it cools.

COCOA BUTTER SUBSTITUTE

Cocoa butter substitute is used as a lubricant to soften skin and as a massage cream. It also protects skin from sun and wind.

4 tablespoons petroleum jelly
6 tablespoons lanolin

Melt the ingredients in a microwave or a double boiler.

CUTICLE SOFTENER

Massage petroleum jelly into the cuticles each morning and night to soften them.

FISH BAIT

Use small pieces of sponge coated with petroleum jelly to simulate fish-egg bait.

FISHING LINE DRESSING

This dressing is used on linen or flax fishing line so that the line will float.

1 teaspoon castor oil
2 tablespoons lanolin
5 teaspoons petroleum jelly

Melt the ingredients in a microwave or in a small can placed in boiling water. Pour the mixture into a paper cup. Rub the line over the dressing, making sure that all areas are coated.

HAIR PRESSING OIL

See page 38.

HONEY OINTMENT

1 part honey
2 parts petroleum jelly

Combine the ingredients. The healing properties of honey and herbs are listed on page 39.

LUBRICANT

Petroleum jelly is a waterproof lubricant that is long lasting.

MOLD RELEASE

See page 66.

MOSQUITO REPELLENT

Almost any oily preparation on the skin repels mosquitoes.

5 tablespoons petroleum jelly
2 tablespoons mineral oil
1 tablespoon citronella essential oil

Stir the ingredients together. Also see page 100 for "Insect Repellent".

PAINT MASK

Before painting around window panes or hardware, apply a thin film of petroleum jelly to protect them from paint. After the paint has dried, the petroleum jelly and any paint over it are easily wiped away.

SELF-SOLDER

This substance is applied to clean surfaces to be soldered. It is then melted with a match or other small flame. No flux is necessary.

Parts by weight:
1 part lead solder shavings
1 part petroleum jelly
1 part ammonium chloride

Mix the ingredients. Ammonium chloride is sold by "Chem Lab" and "Hagenow Laboratories" (see Appendix A).

SOLDERING FLUX

Parts by weight:
1 part ammonium chloride
1 part petroleum jelly

Mix the ingredients. Apply the mixture to clean metal parts that are to be soldered.

SORE MUSCLE RUB

1/4 cup petroleum jelly
1/4 cup lanolin
1 tablespoon wintergreen essential oil

Stir the ingredients together. Apply the formula generously to painful joints and muscles before and after exercise. Massage gently and repeat as needed.

STUCK CAPS

Put a thin layer of petroleum jelly over the threads of tubes and jars. This keeps caps from sticking on such things as glue or oil paint.

VAPOR RUB

The penetrating vapor of this ointment relieves a stuffy nose and chest congestion. It is also a natural moisturizer that protects lips and skin from chapping.

1/2 cup petroleum jelly
2 tablespoons wintergreen, camphor or eucalyptus essential oil
2 teaspoons beeswax

Melt the beeswax and petroleum jelly in a microwave or a double boiler. Remove it from the heat and stir in the essential oil. The oils are available from herb suppliers (see Appendix A). They can be used singularly or in combination. Liberally rub the ointment on the chest, throat and back. Cover the areas with a warm cloth. A little ointment may be applied under the nose if desired.

BEESWAX POLISH

Beeswax polish with its soft, satin shine was once considered the ultimate in wood care. It is fast losing this distinction due to poor products being sold and good products being sold without proper instructions for their use. There is also confusion between beeswax polish formulas designed for bare wood surfaces and formulas designed for sealed wood surfaces. Formulas that contain beeswax, turpentine and *linseed oil* are designed to provide a hand-waxed finish to bare wood. Linseed oil takes days to dry. This old-fashioned and labor-intensive method of finishing wood involves the application of multiple layers of wax and friction polishing between applications (see page 103 for "Wood Finishes"). Hand-waxed finishes permeate wood and provide a finish that is impossible to remove. Hand-waxed finishes still remain on a few glorious antiques, but are rarely seen on modern woodwork.

Modern woodwork is usually sealed with varnish, shellac, paint or synthetic finishes. Most polish formulas for sealed-wood surfaces contain beeswax and turpentine, the amount of turpentine determines if the product is a liquid or a paste. This type of polish is slightly tacky and has the unpleasant odor of turpentine.

Avoid turpentine odor by using low-odor mineral spirits or an odorless turpentine substitute such as Turpenoid® sold by "Sax Arts and Crafts" (see Apppendix A). The addition of essential oils such as pine, lemon or citronella also improves the odor, but use only a small amount. Essential oils slow the drying rate of the polish. Essential oils are sold by herb suppliers (see Appendix A). Never add candle scents to polish formulas. Some of them damage wood finishes.

Adding carnauba wax to beeswax polish formulas solves the tackiness problem and makes buffing much easier. Carnauba wax is very brittle. When struck sharply, it will break and can be measured as a powder. Oil-soluble aniline dye can be added to any polish formula to help conceal scratches in the finish. These dyes are available in many colors from art suppliers such as "Daniel Smith" or wood-finishing suppliers such as "Woodworker's Supply". See Appendix A for suppliers.

Lacquered tins and wide-mouth jars are appropriate containers for cream or paste polish, while small-mouth bottles and squeeze containers are appropriate for liquids. "Brushy Mountain Bee Farm" (see Appendix A) sells beeswax, carnauba wax, lacquered tins and labels for furniture polish. "Sunburst Bottle Company" sells many appropriate containers for cream and liquid polishes. Lye is sold as drain cleaner, but all drain cleaners are not 100% lye. The label should state the content as sodium hydroxide. "Chem Lab" and "Hagenow Laboratory Supply" (see Appendix A) sell lye (sodium hydroxide). See page 93 for "Soap" and read the precautions of handling lye. Mineral spirits is found with paint supplies.

Note: Containers used to melt beeswax are easily cleaned in the dishwasher.

LIQUID POLISH I

4 ounces (weight) beeswax
2 tablespoons carnauba wax
2 1/2 cups mineral spirits or Turpenoid®

Melt the waxes on high in a microwave (watch closely) or in a double boiler. Remove the waxes from the heat and stir in the mineral spirits.

LIQUID POLISH II

4 ounces (weight) beeswax
2 tablespoons carnauba wax
1/8 teaspoon lye (sodium hydroxide)
2 cups water
2 cups mineral spirits or Turpenoid®

Melt the waxes on high in a microwave (watch closely) or in a double boiler. Add lye to the water and stir until it dissolves. Remove the wax from heat and add the lye water. Immediately add the mineral spirits while stirring briskly or by using an electric mixer.

PASTE POLISH I

Use the Liquid Polish I formula, reducing the amount of mineral spirits to 1 1/2 cups.

PASTE POLISH II

Use the Liquid Polish II formula, reducing the amount of water to 1/4 cup and mineral spirits to 1/2 cup.

CREAM POLISH

Make Paste Polish II and allow it to cool. Make small additions of mineral spirits while whipping with an electric mixer or blender until the polish has the consistency of hand cream.

GENERAL DIRECTIONS

These polishes can be used on sealed wood surfaces such as floors, furniture, paneling and other woodwork. Try waxing half of a wooden surface with beeswax and the other half with one of the silicone products that are popular today. The silicone shine will fade in a few days while the beeswax shine may last a year. Liquid polishes and creams can be used to polish metal, chrome, and glass. It is amazing how easy appliances are to clean once they have been waxed. Paste or liquid polish can be used on items made of polished leather, such as shoes (page 46). Never dust a waxed finish with an oiled cloth or it will have to be buffed again with a clean cloth to bring back the shine.

Creams and Liquids: Creams and liquids are easy to apply and they clean as well as polish. Apply the polish with a clean cloth and rub in small circles (6-to-8-inches) over dusty surfaces or surfaces with a slight wax build-up. Turn the cloth as it becomes dirty. Allow the polish to dry, then buff with a clean cloth. Rub in circles and then with the grain of the wood. If your finger leaves a print after buffing, more buffing is required. If more than one coat of polish is desired, allow a few days between each coat for the polish to harden. A quart of liquid polish covers about 40 square feet.

Pastes: Pastes contain more wax than liquids, are long lasting, and provide a harder finish. The surface to be waxed must be clean. The cleaning formula removes years of dirt and wax build-up.

Cleaning Formula

1 cup boiled linseed oil
2/3 cup mineral spirits
1/3 cup vinegar

Mix the ingredients. Store the formula in a closed container. Apply the cleaning mixture to finished wood surfaces with a soft cloth, rubbing to remove dirt and wax build-up. For problem build-up, use 4/0 steel wool. Allow the surface to dry (at least overnight).

Paste waxes are applied the same as liquids, but they are concentrated and a very small amount is applied. If more than one coat of polish is desired, allow a few days between each coat for the polish to harden.

Polishes have a long shelf life, but paste wax may become hard. Place the container in hot water to soften the paste and stir in a small amount of mineral spirits. One pound of paste wax covers about 125 square feet.

October is national mead month.

PROPOLIS

Propolis is gathered by honeybees to seal and disinfect their hives. It contains about 55% resins and balms, 30% wax, 10% etheric oils and 5% pollen. Research has proven that propolis is antibiotic. "Beehive Botanicals" and "Sunstream" sell propolis granules, propolis tincture and propolis gum as well as products containing pollen and royal jelly. Small jars suitable for ointment and lip balm are sold by "Sunburst Bottle Company". See Appendix A for suppliers.

PROPOLIS GRANULES

Propolis granules can be substituted for rosin in most of the formulas in this book.

Step 1: Obtain hive scrapings containing mostly propolis. Place the scrapings in a heat-proof container that can later be discarded. Add enough water to cover the scrapings and heat this in a 200 degree F. oven. The wax will melt and float on the water, while the propolis will stick to the bottom of the container. Stir often to help release the wax. Maintain the heat for at least 2 hours. Remove the can from the oven and let it cool.

Step 2: Remove the waxy layer that formed on the surface of the water. Pour off the water and save the colored mass beneath it.

Step 3: Place the container in a freezer. When the propolis is brittle, chip the granules from the container. Spread the propolis granules on a paper towel to dry. Store them in a sealed container.

PROPOLIS TINCTURE

Step 1: Measure the propolis granules and add an equal measure of 100-proof vodka. Heat the closed bottle in a 200 degree F. oven and shake the bottle every 30 minutes. Maintain the heat until the propolis granules are dissolved and the mixture is uniform.

Step 2: Strain the mixture through filter cloth, paper towel or nylon stocking. Dropper bottles are sold by "Chem Lab" and "Hagenow Laboratories" (see Appendix A). Bottle and label the tincture. The shelf life is several years. Propolis tincture can be used full strength, internally or externally, on cuts, scratches and rashes.

PROPOLIS LIP BALM

1 tablespoon beeswax
1 teaspoon propolis granules
1 teaspoon lanolin
3 tablespoons mineral oil
A few drops wintergreen essential oil

Melt the ingredients in a microwave or make a small double boiler by placing a can in boiling water. Stir until it cools.

PROPOLIS HEALING OINTMENT

1 tablespoon beeswax
4 tablespoons mineral oil
1 tablespoon propolis granules
1 tablespoon honey

Melt the ingredients in a microwave or make a small double boiler by placing a can in boiling water. Stir until it cools.

REFINING BEESWAX

Wax cappings are cut from honeycomb cells to remove the honey beneath them. This light-colored wax is relatively free of impurities (except honey) and desired for the best quality wax. Old comb that has contained brood is dark brown. It contains many impurities such as cocoons and propolis. When old combs are melted, the cocoons act as tiny sponges, holding the melted wax. The cocoons must be squeezed to release the wax. Wax from old combs is lesser quality than wax from cappings. These two waxes should be refined separately.

GENERAL DIRECTIONS

Step 1: Wash cappings within two days of extracting the honey. Pour water over the cappings and stir to mix the honey with the water. Pick out and discard any large black pieces. Strain the cappings. Repeat this step 3 or 4 times to remove as much honey as possible. There is no need to wash old combs.

Step 2: Add 2 inches of water to a large stainless steel or enamel pot. The water allows impurities to settle and the wax to float. Put the cappings or old comb into a straining bag. Pantyhose (with no runs) makes a good bag. Tie the bag closed. Place the bag in the pot with the water. Place the pot in an oven set at the lowest setting (never more than 200 degrees F.) for 1 to 2 hours, or until the wax is melted. Oven temperatures vary greatly. It is wise to use an oven thermometer and check it often to be sure the proper temperature is maintained.

Step 3: Take the pot of melted wax from the oven. Wear thick rubber gloves to remove the bag. Squeeze the bag to remove as much wax as possible. Discard the bag. Return the pot of wax to the oven for 2 more hours. This time allows the stirred-up water and impurities to settle from the wax. Turn off the oven and allow the wax to cool. If the oven is needed for other purposes, the pot of wax may be moved, but be careful not to mix water and impurities into the wax when doing so.

Step 4: Touch the hardened wax. If the wax is warm, the center may be liquid even though the outside is hard. Wait until the wax is completely cool. The wax contracts as it cools and can easily be lifted from the water. Lift the wax and cut off the outer layer of impurities. The wax can be placed in an oven for 5 to 10 minutes to soften the outer layer and to make cutting easier. Place the clean wax aside to dry. Save the dirty cuttings from the wax. It can be used in formulas as "Slumgum" (see page 90). The enameled pot is easily cleaned in a dishwasher. Use refined (clean) beeswax for all formulas unless unrefined (crude) beeswax is stated.

Step 5: To mold the wax (also see page 12), heat it to 160 degrees F. There may be impurities at the bottom of the melted wax. Without stirring it, pour the wax into a mold. Leave 2 to 3 inches of wax in the melting pot. Let the wax cool, remove it from the mold and polish it with a nylon or polyester cloth.

SEALING WAX

In 950 AD, seals were accepted as a sign of authenticity just as signatures are accepted today. Seals are a sign of tradition, signifying dignity and prestige. Today seals are used as a fun, decorative touch to personal letters. Sealing wax adheres to wood, paper, glass and metal. It can be used to create tamper-proof seals for food products.

COLORED SEALING WAX

1/2 ounce (weight) beeswax
3 ounces (weight) blonde shellac
Dry artist's pigment or fresco colors

Melt the beeswax in a microwave. Add the shellac flakes and microwave, stirring every 30 seconds until the mixture is melted (about 2 1/2 minutes total time). Stir in the dry pigment. Judge the amount of pigment to add by the color of the wax. Pour this into molds and let it cool.

METALLIC SEALING WAX

Ounces by weight:
1/2 ounce beeswax
4 ounces blonde shellac
1/4 ounce bronze powder

Warning: Bronze powder is metal. Never put it in a microwave.

Melt the beeswax in a microwave. Add the shellac flakes and microwave, stirring every 30 seconds until the mixture is melted (about 2 1/2 minutes total time). Stir in the bronze powder. Pour this into molds and let it cool.

SCENTED SEALING WAX

Sealing wax is normally odorless when melted. Add 1/4 to 1/2 ounce Peru balsam to either formula when the shellac is added. Peru balsam provides a delightful aroma to melted wax. This balsam is sold by herb suppliers such as "Penn Herb" (see Appendix A).

GENERAL DIRECTIONS

Ingredients in these formulas are measured by weight. A small postage or food scale is good to weigh such small amounts. The containers and stirring utensils used to make these formulas are difficult to clean. Use items that can be discarded.

Color: Bronze powder is made from flaked particles of brass, copper and aluminum. The powder is available in the natural metal colors, plus gold and silver. Stir the powder into the melted mixture just before molding the sealing wax. Artist's dry pigments, fresco colors and bronze powders are sold by artist's suppliers such as "Daniel Smith" and by wood-finishing suppliers such as "Woodworker's Supply" (see Appendix A).

Shellac is available in different grades (colors). Blonde shellac is almost clear and allows the pigment in the formula to show through properly. If a dark pigment is used it can be combined with the less expensive orange or garnet shellac. Beeswax, bronze powder, and shellac are sold by wood-finishing suppliers such as

"Woodworker's Supply" (see Appendix A).

Check the telephone book yellow pages for stationery stores. Most of them sell metal seals designed to imprint sealing wax. Initials are a popular seal. Coins, crests of rings and other metal objects can imprint sealing wax.

Molding: Sealing wax is molded the same as a candle (with a wick in the center). A self-contained wick is not essential. Sealing wax can be melted over a flame, such as a cigarette lighter. Several sheets of aluminum foil can be used as a mold. Shape the foil into a mold about 1/4 inch wide and 6 inches long. Lubricate the mold with cooking oil.

Applying Sealing Wax: Work over a level surface that won't be damaged if melted sealing wax falls on it. Light the wick of the sealing wax and hold it downward, at an angle. Put 10 to 15 drops of wax on the surface to be impressed. Extinguish the flame. Wait a few seconds for the wax to cool. Moisten the metal seal, lightly press it into the soft wax and lift it. If the wax cooled too quickly to get a good impression, simply repeat the process. Dropping hot sealing wax onto the failed impression heats the entire mass and it can then be imprinted again. If wax stuck to the metal seal, the wax was too hot. Repeat the process and allow more time for the wax to cool before impressing it.

To make the raised design stand out even more, go over it with a colored marker.

CORKS

This formula makes corks waterproof, gas- and air-tight and easily cut or drilled.

Parts by weight:
7 parts beeswax
2 parts petroleum jelly

Melt the ingredients to 180 degrees F. and immerse the dry corks. Place a weight over the corks to hold them under the wax for at least 5 minutes or until bubbles stop rising. Wear thick rubber gloves to remove the corks from the wax. Wipe them with paper towels to remove excess wax and place them on a rack to cool.

GLASS BOTTLE STOPPERS

Ounces by weight:
1 ounce beeswax
1 ounce glycerin

Melt the ingredients. Dip glass bottle stoppers into the melted mixture to make them air-tight.

TAMPER-PROOF SEALS

To make a container tamper-proof, wrap a label, ribbon or strip of paper vertically around the cap (lid). Tack this into place with glue or rubber cement. Apply sealing wax to fabric, glass, paper, wood or metal and imprint it as desired. Sealing wax works best if the items to be imprinted are room temperature or warmer.

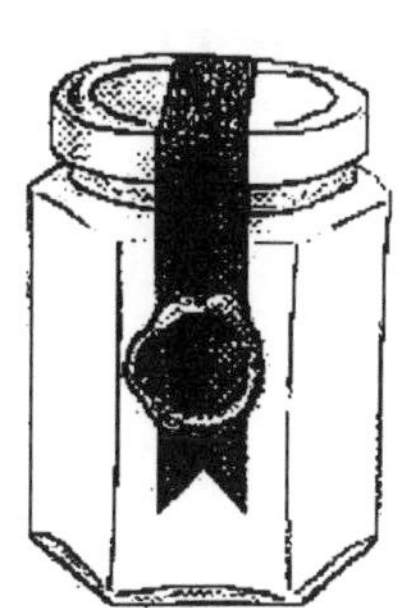

SKEP-MAKING

A straw skep decorating an herb garden.

Until the late 1800's, beekeepers housed colonies of bees in dome-shaped straw containers called *skeps*. The name skep is believed to have come from the Norse word *skeppa* meaning a measure for grain. In 1851, Lorenzo L. Langstroth's invention of the movable frame hive revolutionized beekeeping, and beekeepers quickly abandoned skeps in favor of the new hive. Today, an empty skep is often used to decorate an herb garden. Check with the local bee authority before housing bees in skeps. Skeps are sold by "Brushy Mountain Bee Farm" and herb suppliers such as "Dabney Herbs" and "The Rosemary House" (see Appendix A).

EQUIPMENT AND SUPPLIES

The following are sold by basket-making suppliers such as "Earth Guild" (see Appendix A).

- ❑ Straw
- ❑ #4 binder cane
- ❑ Basket weaving needle
  or a very large, sharp tapestry needle

Straw for making skeps should be harvested in the fall. Rye, oats, barley and wheat straw are often used. Whatever mixed grain that grows along the roadside will probably be suitable. A large armful or a 5-gallon bucket full should be enough to make one skep. Remove any leaves, sheaths or flowers. Skeps can be made of 1-inch rope. Originally skeps were bound with bramble cane which was stripped of thorns and split. Number 4 binder cane is a good substitute or any thin, flexible cane about 1/8-inch wide and about 6-feet long. Strong cord or twine may also be used to bind coils.

GENERAL DIRECTIONS

Step 1: Put the coil of binder cane in the bottom of a bucket to keep it from becoming tangled. Soak the cane and the straw in warm water until it is pliable enough to form a 6-inch circle without breaking.

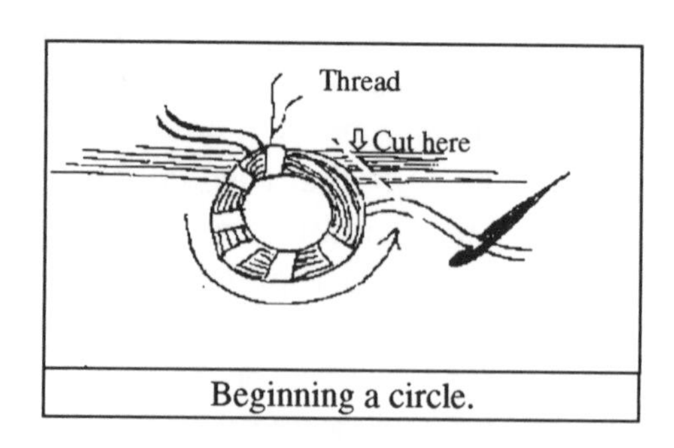

Beginning a circle.

Step 2: Beginning a circle. Push an end of binder cane through the eye of the needle. Take enough straw to equal a 1-inch thickness. Offset the ends and form a coil two fingers will fit into. Pass the needle through the circle and in an anti-clockwise direction, tightly wind the cane over and under the coil and the loose end of the binder cane to cover it. Cut the short end of straw from the circle and cover the place with binder cane. Mark the point of beginning with colored thread. From this point all changes in shape and stitch increases are made.

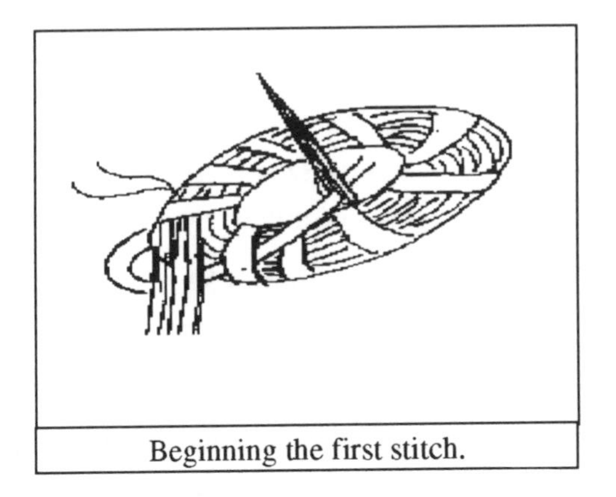
Beginning the first stitch.

Step 3: Stitching. To stitch, work from left to right. Angle the needle and insert it from left to right through the bottom of the stitch in the previous row. Be sure that the needle also goes through part of the straw as it goes through the stitch. The tighter the stitches, the stronger the skep will be. Draw each stitch tight before tightening a new one and try to keep the spaces between the stitches even. Repeat over all the stitches in the row, adding new bunches of straw to the coil to maintain the 1-inch diameter. To end and start a cane, use no knots. Carry the end of the cane with the coil of straw for 3 to 4 inches.

Step 4: Increasing stitches. Basketry is spiral in construction. As the skep increases in size, the stitches radiate and become farther apart. As the diameter of the circle increases, it will be necessary to increase the number of stitches. When the stitches are 2 to 3 inches apart, insert a new stitch just to the left of the thread marking the point of beginning, halfway between the old stitches.

St. Ambrose is the patron saint of beekeepers.

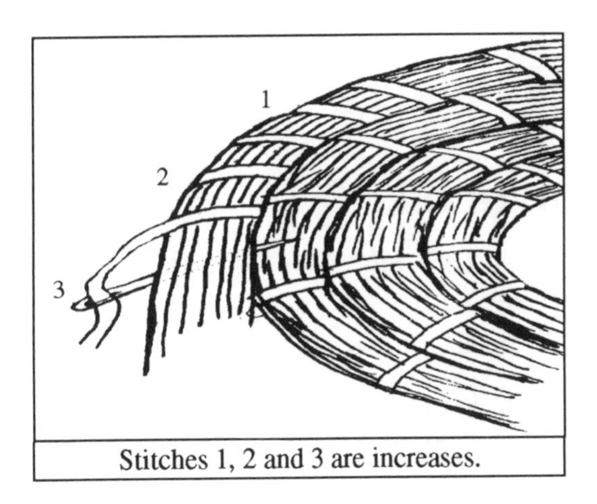

Stitches 1, 2 and 3 are increases.

Continue the increase between each stitch until the row is complete. The succeeding rows follow both the old and the new stitches thus established. Keep the coil flat until it is about 9 inches in diameter.

Step 5: Dome shaping. The shaping of the skep is done entirely with the left hand, securely fastening the coil into position with firm stitches and always starting from the point of beginning. Hold the new coil on top and to the outside of the previous round. Angle the needle to gradually widen and shape the dome. When the stitches are too far apart, more are added between each of the stitches in one complete row. Continue until a bowl-shape, 12 inches in diameter is formed.

Step 6: Straight Sides and Ending: Add coils directly on top of one another and keep the needle at a right angle to the work. The number of stitches stays the same for perpendicular rounds until the desired height is obtained. When the desired height is obtained, continue the stitches without adding new reeds to the coil. The coil will get thinner and blend into the skep edge. End the cane by running it through several inches of straw inside the skep.

SKIN CARE

BATH OIL

Most bath oils float on water. This oil mixes with water, clings to the skin and forms a thin, even coating.

1 whole egg
1/2 cup mineral oil
2 teaspoons liquid soap or detergent
1/4 cup vodka
2 tablespoons honey
1/4 cup whole milk
Fragrant essential oil (optional)

Mix ingredients in a blender for 30 seconds. Use only 1 or 2 tablespoons of the oil in a bathtub of water.

CALLUS REMOVER

This formula removes tough calluses.

1 ounce (weight) beeswax
1/2 cup castor or mineral oil
1 tablespoon liquid soap
1 teaspoon sodium thiosulfate crystals

Melt the oil and wax in a microwave and add the remaining ingredients. Rub the mixture onto the callus and apply a bandage. The next morning, soak the callus in hot, soapy water. Repeat the treatment until the callus is removed. Sodium thiosulfate is sold by chemical suppliers such as "Hagenow Laboratories" and "Chem Lab" (see Appendix A).

CLEANSING GRAINS

If after a bath, a towel rub shows pills of dead skin cells, cleansing grains should have been used weeks ago. Cleansing grains clear away dead skin cells and blackheads. Their abrasiveness stimulates circulation. They are used as facials or as all-over body rubs. Chose one of the following.

♦ **For Dry Skin**
Equal measures of sugar, honey and oil.

♦ **For Normal Skin**
Equal measures of sugar and honey.

♦ **For Oily Skin**
Equal measures of salt, honey and liquid soap or detergent.

Combine the ingredients for a skin type. The measures can be teaspoons or half-cups. Open the pores of the skin with a hot bath or a facial sauna. Use a warm, wet washcloth to gently rub the cleansing grains onto the skin. Wait 5 to 10 minutes and rinse well. Follow this treatment with an astringent, a toning lotion or a cool-water splash to close the pores of the skin.

MOISTURIZING FACIAL

Honey is hygroscopic (it attracts moisture) and antibacterial. Mix 1 tablespoon honey with 1 tablespoon hot water. Apply the mixture, wait 30 minutes and rinse well.

SOAP SUBSTITUTE

This formula cleans and softens skin without the drying effects of soap. It is suitable for all skin types and can be used for hands, baths or facials.

3 tablespoons cornmeal
2 tablespoons honey
1 tablespoon cornstarch
Fragrant essential oil (optional)

Mix the ingredients. Wet the skin, rub the soap substitute over it and rinse well.

SKIN CREAM

Cold cream was the first skin cream. It dates back to prehistoric times and was used as a cleanser. Cold cream was mixed into dirt on the skin and both were wiped away. Today cold cream is seldom used. Beauty experts agree that cold cream does a poor job of removing dirty surface film. Cold cream is difficult to remove and a film of dirty cream is always left on the skin surface.

Cold cream does a good job of holding skin moisture. "Ultra-rich Skin Cream" is based on cold cream formulas. This cream is ultra-rich due to the addition of lanolin. Of all natural raw materials, lanolin is the most similar to human skin and hair fat, both in chemical composition and in physiological properties. It is a natural skin emollient. Lanolin relieves chapped lips, chapped and cracked hands, diaper rash, windburn and minor skin irritations. Only a small amount is applied to clean skin. It does not wash off easily.

ULTRA-RICH SKIN CREAM

2 1/2 ounces (weight) beeswax
4 ounces (weight) anhydrous lanolin
2/3 cup baby oil
3/4 cup water
1 teaspoon borax (sodium borate, C.P.)
Fragrant essential oil (optional)

Borax is sold with laundry detergents, but chemically pure borax, which is required for cosmetics, is sold by drug stores and "Chem Lab" (see Appendix A). Lanolin is sold by drug stores. In a microwave or double boiler, melt the oil, lanolin and beeswax to 160 degrees F. Heat the borax and water in a separate container to 160 degrees F. Be sure the borax is dissolved and the wax is melted. Add the water mixture to the oil mixture while stirring briskly. When white cream forms, stir slowly until the mixture cools to 100 degrees F. Pour it into small, wide-mouth jars.

Oil Substitutions: Use a variety of oils as long as their combination equals 2/3 cup. Baby oil is simply mineral oil plus fragrance. "Haussmann's Pharmacy" sells herbs, beeswax, many oils and 1-pound units of lanolin at a reasonable price (see Appendix A). The cream can be colored pink by replacing a small amount of the mineral oil with "Alkanet Colored Oil" (see page 52).

Water Substitutions: Fragrance and other characteristics of herbs may be introduced to the cream (see page 39 for herbs and page 28 for essential oils). Boil 1 cup of water for 15 minutes. Introduce the herb or fragrant material. The amount varies according to the strength of the material selected. Cover this and allow it to cool. Filter through a coffee filter or a paper towel. Use 3/4 cup to replace the water requested in the basic formula. Fresh fruit or vegetable juices are not recommended as water substitutions due to spoilage factors.

Containers: "Brush Mountain Bee Farm" and "Sunburst Bottle Company" (see Appendix A) sell small attractive jars suitable for creams and cosmetics.

SLUMGUM

Slumgum is a waste product of refining beeswax. It cannot be purchased by mail. See page 83 for "Refining Beeswax".

COMPOST

Slumgum that crumbles is relatively wax free. It is biodegradable and can be added to compost piles.

DANCE FLOOR POWDER

Broadcast this powder over the dance floor before dancing begins and leave it in place during the dance.

8 ounces (weight) crude beeswax
or wax-rich slumgum
3 1/2 pounds boric acid powder
2 tablespoons lavender essential oil

Melt the wax in a microwave or double boiler. Remove the wax from the heat and stir in the lavender oil. Stir in the boric acid and let the mixture cool. Rub the mixture through screen mesh. Chemically pure boric acid from the druggist is expensive. Order technical grade boric acid powder from "Chem Lab" (see Appendix A).

FIRE KINDLING I

Parts by weight:
3 parts crude beeswax or slumgum
1 part rosin, pitch or propolis scrapings
6 parts wood flour or fine sawdust

Melt the beeswax and rosin in an oven set at 225 degrees F. Stir in the wood flour. While the mixture is warm, press it tightly into molds to form sticks.

FIRE KINDLING II

Many items can be used as kindling when dipped into melted slumgum. Try dipping pieces of cardboard, pine cones, and twisted sheets of paper.

FIRE KINDLING III

Fill the compartments of paper egg cartons with sawdust. While stirring the sawdust, pour in melted slumgum. Allow this to cool and tear apart the compartments, leaving the paper attached. To start a fire light the paper.

SWEEPING COMPOUND

Sprinkle this mixture on a floor and use a push mop to sweep. This can be used repeatedly until it becomes too dirty.

Parts by weight:
1 part crude beeswax or slumgum
10 parts sand
5 parts sawdust
4 parts light motor oil

Melt the wax and oil together in a double boiler or an oven set at 200 degree F. Stir the mixture into the sawdust and mix well. Add the sand and more sawdust if the mixture is too damp. Do not store this floor sweeping compound near flames or extreme heat.

Twelve honeybees must work their entire lifetime to make one teaspoon of honey.

SOAP-MAKING

Little soap was available during World War II due to shortages of animal fats and vegetable oils. Germany introduced synthetic detergents made from petroleum chemicals reacted with sulfuric acid. The public immediately accepted detergents. Today dishwashing detergents, laundry detergents, shampoos, bath bubbles, household cleansers and most bath bars are synthetic detergents. Detergents are so common that many people have never used soap.

Homemade soap feels good: soft, rich and soothing. The lather is dense rather than thin and airy. Soap leaves an emollient film on the skin that makes it feel soft and sensuous. The following soap formulas are mild bath bars suitable for sensitive skin. Please read the entire chapter before attempting to make soap. Each formula makes about 8 bars.

Recommended Reading
Soap: Making it, Enjoying it
by Ann Bramson

"Pourette" sells molds, scents and aniline dyes. They also sell a good booklet, "Soapreme: Your Own Handmade Soap with Custom Molds". Request their *soap* making catalog as their main catalog lists candle-making supplies. "Sun Feather Herbal Soap Company" sells sodium hydroxide, oils, tallow and essential oils for soap-making (see Appendix A).

BEESWAX SKIN SOAP

Ounces by weight:
1 ounce beeswax
6 ounces olive oil
6 ounces coconut oil

Homemade soap in many shapes and colors.

9.5 ounces tallow
3 1/2 ounces lye (sodium hydroxide)
8 ounces water
2 teaspoons fragrant essential oil

Add lye to the water and wait for it to cool to 160 degrees F. Melt the beeswax. Weigh and combine the oils and tallow. Mix in the melted beeswax. Heat the oils to 130 degrees F. Slowly pour the lye water into the fat mixture while stirring. Stir for 20 minutes, add the fragrant oil, and pour the soap into molds. Harden the soap in a freezer for 2 to 3 hours. The soap is harsh at this point so wear rubber gloves and remove the soap from the molds. Place it on unprinted cardboard or paper bags to age at least two weeks.

MILK AND HONEY SPICE BARS

Ounces by weight:
12 ounces coconut oil
9 ounces tallow
3 ounces lye (sodium hydroxide)
8 ounces milk (goat or cow)
1 tablespoon honey
2 teaspoons cinnamon essential oil

Add the lye to the milk and allow it to

cool to 140 degrees F. Melt the oils and fats to 140 degrees F. Slowly pour the lye milk into the fat solution while stirring. Stir for 20 minutes, add the cinnamon oil, and pour the soap into molds. Place it in a freezer to harden for 2 to 3 hours. Wear rubber gloves and remove the soap from the molds. Place the soap on unprinted cardboard or paper bags to age at least two weeks. With no coloring added, the oils make this soap a spicy brown color.

VEGETARIANS' SOAP

Ounces by weight:
11 ounces coconut oil
4.5 ounces olive oil
6 ounces vegetable shortening
3 3/4 ounces lye (sodium hydroxide)
8 ounces water
2 teaspoons fragrant essential oil

Add the lye to the water and allow it to cool to 150 degrees F. Melt the oils to 150 degrees F. Slowly pour the lye water into the oils while stirring. Stir for 20 minutes, add the fragrant oil, and pour the soap into molds. Put the soap in a freezer for 2 to 3 hours to harden. Wear rubber gloves and remove the soap from the molds. Place the soap on unprinted cardboard or paper bags to age.

FACIAL SCRUB

Before pouring the soap into molds, add 1 cup cornmeal, flaked oats or cream of wheat. The grains are gently abrasive and the starch is soothing.

HERB AND SPICE SOAP

Before pouring the soap, stir in up to 1/2 cup of dried, finely ground herbs or spices.

LAUNDRY POWDER

1 part bar soap, finely grated
3 parts borax

Borax is sold with laundry detergents. Use this powder in warm or hot water. Add 1/2 cup vinegar to the washing machine's fabric softener dispenser.

OATMEAL SOAP

Before pouring the soap, beat in 1/2 cup dry baby oatmeal.

PUMICE SOAP

Before pouring the soap, beat in 1 to 2 cups of 2F pumice, available from "Woodworker's Supply" (see Appendix A). This soap removes tough dirt and grease from hands.

SHAMPOO BAR

Soap is a good shampoo bar. Use one of the following rinses to remove soap residue.

♦ For dark hair
1/4 cup vinegar to 3/4 cup water.
♦ For light hair
The juice from 1 lemon to 1 cup water.

SHAVING SOAP

Pour 3 to 4 inches of soap into a mug. Allow the soap to harden and age in the mug. Use the soap with a shaving brush.

SUPER-FATTED SOAP

Add 1/4 cup of oil to the basic formula. The extra oil is unaffected by the lye. This soap is suitable for dry skin, makeup removal or shaving.

WATERLESS HAND CLEANSER

3/4 cup soap
1/2 cup oil
1 cup water

Use soap that is still soft. Instead of pouring it into molds, combine it with the oil and water by beating it with an electric mixer. Pour this into tubs, wide-mouth jars or liquid soap dispensers. Take about 1 teaspoon of the cleanser and rub it into the dirt or grease. Wipe the hands dry with a paper towel.

GENERAL DIRECTIONS

WARNING: Lye can burn your skin, remove paint and generate heat. Wear goggles and rubber gloves to make soap. If lye gets on your skin, rinse it off with vinegar.

Lye: Look where drain cleaners are sold and buy 100% lye (sodium hydroxide); "Red Devil" is one brand name or order sodium hydroxide from a chemical supplier such as "Chem Lab" and "Hagenow Laboratories" (see Appendix A). Read and follow the precautions on the can. Add lye to the liquid while stirring to prevent the lye from hardening in the bottom of the container. Use only heat-proof stone, glass, enamel or stainless steel containers. For stirring, use rubber, plastic or wooden spoons. Never heat lye water in the microwave. Set the container in a sink of hot water if necessary.

Molds: Lye reacts with most metals. Never use Teflon, iron, aluminum or tin as a mold. Do use heat-proof stone, glass, enamel, stainless steel or plastic. Freezing soap keeps it from separating and allows easy removal from the mold.

Coconut oil is sold in grocery stores with cooking oils. Restaurants order it in 5-gallon buckets at 70 cents per pound. A mail order source is "Vinton Popcorn Company," telephone (319) 472-5235.

Tallow: Tallow is rendered fat. Some butchers will give beef fat free of charge if they know it is for soap-making. Cut the fat in 2-to-3-inch pieces. Place it in a large pot with about 2 cups water. Cook over medium heat until the water evaporates and the fat pieces are brown. Strain the fat and place it in the refrigerator or freezer to harden. Lift the hardened fat from the water. Scrape any impurities from the top and bottom of the fat. Tallow will keep for months in the refrigerator and for years in the freezer.

Coloring: "Pourette", "Daniel Smith" and "Earth Guild" (see Appendix A) sell water-soluble aniline dye used to color soap Dissolve the dye in water before adding the lye. About 1/4 teaspoon dye per soap formula yields a medium color shade. This color shade may seem too dark at first, but soap lightens considerably with age.

Hardening and Aging: Soap is semi-liquid when poured. Aging allows the soap to harden and allows time for lye to react with the fats. Wash off the white coating that may form before using or testing the soap.

Testing Soap: Test soap by sticking it to the tongue. If there is a burning sensation, something went wrong with the temperatures, measurements, or the amount of stirring. Further aging may allow the soap to become milder. Large bars of soap can be mild on the outside while still being harsh inside. They require longer aging than smaller bars.

SOFT DRINKS

Wine-making supply catalogs (Appendix A) list champagne yeast and flavor extracts used to make soft drinks. Extracts, honey and champagne yeast combine to produce natural carbonation within the bottles. Naturally-carbonated soft drinks must be stored in a refrigerator and are best consumed within 2 months of bottling. Available flavors are: cola, ginger ale, lemon-line, raspberry, sarsaparilla, strawberry, creme soda, ginger beer, orange, root beer, spruce beer and wild cherry.

GENERAL DIRECTIONS

2 quarts water
1 pound (weight) or 1 1/2 cups honey
1 tablespoon soft drink extract
1/8 teaspoon champagne yeast

Obtain a plastic 2-liter soda bottle with a plastic cap. Mix the water, extract and honey in the bottle. Dissolve the yeast in 1 cup water at 115 degrees F. while stirring (about 3 minutes) and pour it into the bottle. Cap the bottle and shake it to mix the contents.

Store the soft drink upright at room temperature for 2 to 3 days or until carbonation pressure makes the bottle very firm. Then place it upright in a refrigerator to arrest yeast activity. At serving time, open the bottle slowly to gradually release pressure and to avoid foaming. The bottle contains a sediment of yeast. Pour all but the last inch of soft drink to allow the yeast to remain in the bottom of the bottle.

TEMPERATURE CONTROL

It is often difficult to maintain temperatures between 32 and 99 degrees F. "The Cellar" (see Appendix A) and businesses that sell window air conditioner units sell a digital temperature control that can be used with an air conditioner, a heater, refrigerator, or freezer to hold preset temperatures. The control plugs into an electrical outlet and the appliance plugs into the control. The control has a temperature sensor on a four-foot long wire. The sensor can be placed in a room, inside a box, or inside a refrigerator or freezer. The control maintains any set temperature by turning the appliance off and on. A light bulb inside an insulated box can maintain temperatures from 70 to 99 degrees F. The control can be used to maintain important temperatures required for the following.

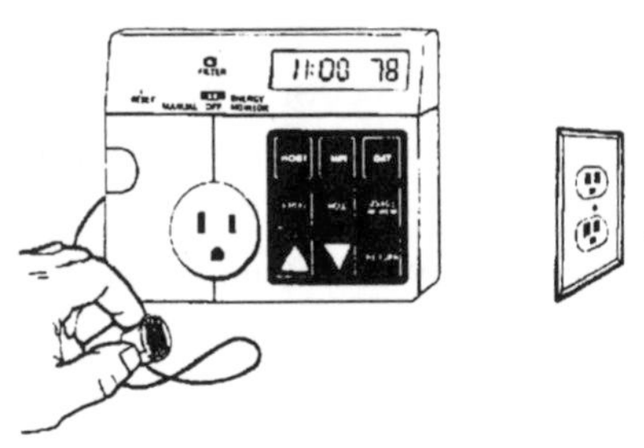

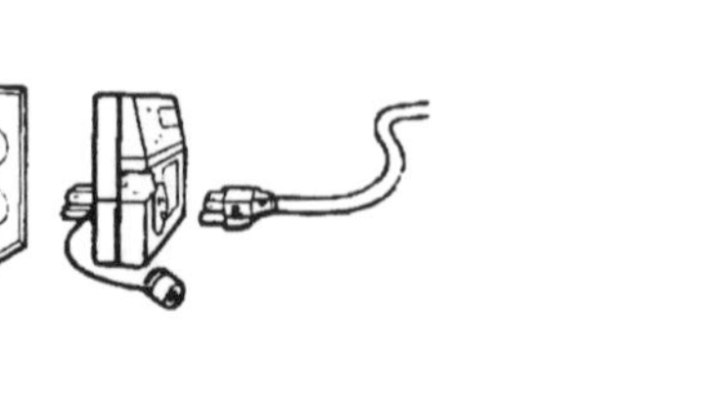

Brewing beer
Making cheese
Heating honey for extraction
Making creamed honey
Making vinegar
Rising yeast breads
Softening modeling wax
Warming wax sheets
Making wine

UKRAINIAN EASTER EGGS

The people of Poland, the Ukraine, and other Slavic nations use a wax-resist method to elaborately decorate Easter eggs. This practice began long before Christ and later incorporated religious symbols into the egg designs. *Pysanky* and *krashanky* are the most widely known.

Krashanky (plural of *krashanka*) are hard-boiled eggs, dyed a solid color, which are eaten. Peasants placed krashanky shells on roofs to turn away high winds, and beekeepers put them under beehives for a good supply of honey.

Pysanky (plural of *pysanka*) are elaborately decorated raw eggs. Traditionally they are not eaten. Dots are often incorporated into the designs in honor of Mary's tears. A bowl of pysanky is kept as protection against lightning and fire. Pysanky are exchanged at Easter with the words "Christ is risen," and the reply, "He is risen indeed."

The following directions are for pysanky, the elaborately decorated, raw eggs that are not eaten. The vibrant colors used to make pysanky are not food safe. The wax-resist method of dyeing pysanky is very similar to methods used for batik. See page 5 for "Batik" where the process is outlined in detail and page 17 where a helpful color chart is found.

EQUIPMENT AND SUPPLIES

The supplies and tools are sold by "Surma" and "Earth Guild" (see Appendix A).

- ❑ *Tjanting* or *kiska* (Drawing page 6)
- ❑ Beeswax
- ❑ Water-soluble aniline dye or cold-water fabric dye

GENERAL DIRECTIONS

Eggs: Use farm-fresh eggs if possible. Some eggs from the grocery store have been treated with an oil-like substance and do not accept color very well. Test the egg by coloring it a very light shade of yellow or pink (see Step 5). The color should be even with no blotches or scratches. Whole raw eggs may be used for pysanky. Place the eggs out of the way, at room temperature, for one year. Some of the eggs will crack and fall apart. The others remain whole and are ready for decoration. Fresh, raw eggs may be emptied by piercing the top and bottom of the egg and blowing through one of the holes to remove the contents.

Step 1: Mix 2 tablespoons vinegar into 1 cup water. Rinse the hands and eggs in the mixture. Allow the eggs to air dry.

Step 2: Place a small can in an electric skillet set at 300 degrees F. or in a pot of boiling water. Place beeswax in the can to melt.

Step 3: The eggs and room should be 70 to 80 degrees F. Use a pencil to draw lines and designs on the egg. Wide rubber bands can be used as guides. Do not erase, or that area will not accept dye properly.

Step 4: Practice applying melted wax with a tjanting over a smooth surface similar to the egg shell. Keep the tjanting at a right angle to the surface. After sufficient practice, apply melted wax to the egg. Designs formed by this waxing preserve the color beneath the wax. If a mistake is made while applying the wax, incorporate the mistake into the design. The wax cannot be removed.

Step 5: Prepare the dye. Use water-soluble aniline dye or cold-water fabric dye. Dissolve 1/4 to 1/2 teaspoon dye in a few tablespoons of boiling water. Add enough cold water to equal one cup. Add 1 tablespoon vinegar and mix well.

Step 6: Place the egg in the dye and leave it until the desired color is obtained. Remove the egg and rinse it under running water. Let the egg dry completely before going to the next step. Wax will not adhere to wet surfaces.

Step 7: Again form designs on the egg with melted wax. Designs formed by this waxing protects the color of the dye under the wax. Repeat Steps 6 and 7 as many times as desired. Traditionally, black is used as the last color.

Step 8: When the dye process is complete, place the egg on absorbent paper toweling. Set an oven at 250 degrees F. and place the egg and toweling in the oven. When the wax is melted, blot the egg with a paper towel to remove the melted wax. If desired, apply a clear protective coat of spray varnish over the egg.

PAINTING WITH DYE

Dark colors of red, green and blue should be painted within waxed outlines. Allow the dye to dry completely and cover it with beeswax to keep this color from mixing with the next dye color.

SYMBOLIC COLOR AND DESIGN

Colors are significant in pysanky. Green means money; purple, power; orange, attraction; black, remembrance; blue, health; brown, happiness; white, purity; red, love; pink, success; and yellow, spirituality. Pysanky designs usually suggest an object rather than picture it exactly.

####### ▦
Checkerboard or sieve, for filling in.
⊙ ⊙ ⊙ O O O ✳ ✳ ✳
The circle, poppy and spider web represent the sun and good fortune.
• • • ∴ ∴ ∴ ∴∴O O O 0 0 0
Dots, specks, circles or ovals represent stars or Mary's tears.
====================
Ribbons or belts represent eternity.
ΔVΔVΔVΔVΔVΔVΔV
Triangles represent the Trinity.
❋ ❋ ❋ ✱ ✱ ✱ ✿
Flowers stand for love and charity.
Wheat means eternal youth and health.
Hens mean the fulfillment of wishes.
Reindeer symbolize prosperity.

VINEGAR-MAKING

In the late 1800's, manufacturer's learned to make acetic acid. They added water to reduce its strength to 5%, colored it and sold it as vinegar. Imitation vinegar is still manufactured, and by law the label should state that it is diluted acetic acid. It is cheap and lacks the vitamins, minerals and esters found in fermented vinegar. Imitation vinegar is also inferior in taste and flavor.

It takes good alcohol (wine or beer) to make fermented vinegar. The "hit or miss" method of making vinegar by allowing honey and water to ferment is not wise. The fermentation of honey to alcohol by wild yeast is followed by a conversion of the alcohol to acetic acid by wild bacteria. Chances of failure or undesirable tastes and aromas are high. Control the process by using great care in cleanliness and introducing chosen yeast and bacteria to obtain quality vinegar every time. Fermented vinegar can be sold without special permits or licenses. It costs the same as a good bottle of wine.

GENERAL DIRECTIONS

Wine-making suppliers (see Appendix A) list *acetobacter* as "mother" or vinegar culture. These cultures convert alcohol to acetic acid (vinegar). Most suppliers sell red and white wine vinegar cultures. "Beer and Winemaking Supplies" (see Appendix A) sells cider, malt and mead cultures as well. Any culture may be combined with any type of alcohol to produce vinegar.

Vinegar should contain at least 5% acid as required for preserving or pickling. Specialty vinegar contains acid as high as 7%. Beer containing 5 1/2% alcohol will yield about 5% acid. Wine containing 11 to 12% alcohol must be diluted to 5 1/2% to 7% alcohol before using it to make vinegar.

Acid test kits, sold by wine-making suppliers, are used to determine the acidity of vinegar. Acid tests are easy to perform and instructions come with the kits.

SANITIZE

Sanitize utensils and containers that will touch the vinegar by soaking them for 15 minutes in a solution of 1 tablespoon chlorine laundry bleach to 1 gallon of water. Rinse everything in hot tap water.

VINEGAR METHOD I

3 measures beer, ale or vinegar stock
(5 1/2 to 7% alcohol)
1 measure vinegar culture
with active bacteria

Directions: Vinegar leaches molecules from iron and aluminum. Use sanitized glass, enamel, stainless steel or stoneware containers less than 2/3 full. Cover the container with a cloth or stopper it with cotton to keep insects out, while allowing air to freely reach the stock. Store the mixture in a dark place.

Temperatures between 80 and 85 degrees F. are ideal. Low or fluctuating temperatures slow the process. At 75 to 85 degrees F., it will take 4 to 6 months for conversion. At 85 to 90 degrees F., it will take 2 to 3 months for conversion.

Temperatures over 95 degrees F. slow conversion and above 140 degrees F. the bacteria die (see page 94 for temperature control).

The leathery film of acetobacter called "mother"or "vinegar plant."

An acetic film called "mother" will form. This smooth, leathery, grayish film becomes quite thick and heavy. It should not be disturbed. It often becomes heavy enough to fall and is succeeded by another formation. If the mother falls, remove and discard it. An acid test will indicate when the alcohol is converted to vinegar. Part of the vinegar may be withdrawn and pasteurized. The remaining vinegar may be used as a culture to start another batch. Living bacteria are in the liquid. A piece of the mother is not necessary to start a new batch.

Add beer or diluted wine to the culture every 3 to 6 months depending on the temperature that is maintained and when most of the alcohol is converted to vinegar. Adding more alcohol to the culture keeps it alive, prevents spoilage and increases the quantity of vinegar. If unpasteurized vinegar is exposed to oxygen without alcohol present, bacteria convert the vinegar to carbon dioxide and water.

VINEGAR METHOD II

2 measures dry wine (11 to 12% alcohol)
1 measure water (boiled and cooled)
1 measure vinegar culture
with active bacteria

Follow the directions in Method I. Purchased wine can be used, but some commercial wines contain sulfites or preservatives that could kill the vinegar bacteria.

VINEGAR METHOD III

For Winemakers Only

Mead Stock for Vinegar

1 1/2 pounds honey or
a specific gravity reading of 1.050
2 teaspoons yeast nutrient or energizer
4 teaspoons acid blend or 7.5 p.p.t.
tartaric with an acid test kit
1/4 teaspoon tannin
Wine yeast
Water to equal 1 gallon

Mead containing less than 10% alcohol is subject to spoilage. This mead formula with 7% alcohol is an ideal vinegar stock. Follow good winemaking procedures (see page 53 for "Mead"). When the fermentation is complete (specific gravity 1.000 or below), this low-alcohol mead is converted to vinegar as directed in Method I.

Homemade Wine

Dry mead containing 11 to 12% alcohol, can be diluted after fermentation (specific gravity 1.000 or below). It does not have to be clear as this is accomplished when the vinegar is aged. At the last racking, do not add campden tablets or potassium sorbate. Dilute the mead as directed in Method II and follow the directions in Method I.

PRESERVING VINEGAR

Pasteurized or sulphited vinegar can no longer produce more vinegar. Pasteurizing kills vinegar bacteria and prevents the formation of "mother" that could lead to spoilage. Pasteurized vinegar keeps indefinitely when tightly capped and stored in a dark place at room temperature. Temperatures above 160 degrees F. cause a loss of acidity, flavor and aroma.

To Preserve Vinegar

Add 2 campden tablets per gallon of vinegar. Campden tablets are sold by wine-making suppliers (see Appendix A).

-------------------OR-------------------

Heat the vinegar to 150 degrees F. and hold that temperature for 30 minutes.

After pasteurizing vinegar, add 1 tablespoon 80-proof vodka to each gallon and age it. If desired to enhance the bouquet, up to 1 cup oak or beech chips may also be added.

AGING VINEGAR

Vinegar has a strong, sharp bite when first made, but becomes mellow when aged. The esters formed during aging, like those in wine, develop after a period of 6 months or more when stored at a cool, steady temperature (50 to 60 degrees F. is ideal). This undisturbed rest also allows suspended solids to fall, making the vinegar clear and bright. Siphon the clear, aged vinegar off the deposit of solids into sanitized bottles. Introduce as little oxygen as possible. Wine-making suppliers sell attractive vinegar bottles. Use corks or plastic caps to avoid contacting the vinegar with metal. If corks are used, the necks of the vinegar bottles should be dipped several times into melted wax to form an airtight seal.

COLORING VINEGAR

See page 33 for caramel food coloring.

USING VINEGAR

ALUMINUM DISCOLORATION

Remove dark stains on aluminum by boiling the item in a solution of 1/4 cup vinegar to 1 quart water.

BUTTERMILK OR SOUR MILK SUBSTITUTE

If a recipe for baking asks for sour or buttermilk and only sweet milk is available, the following can be substituted.

1 tablespoon vinegar
1 cup sweet milk

Stir the ingredients together and let the mixture stand about 5 minutes to clabber.

CHEESE PRESERVATIVE

Moisten paper towels with vinegar and wrap them around cheese. Seal this in a plastic bag and store it in the refrigerator. Moisten the towels as necessary. The vinegar does not affect the taste of the cheese while it prevents mold and keeps the cheese from hardening and drying.

DRIED HERB OR DRIED SPICE VINEGAR

1 quart vinegar
2 to 3 tablespoons dried herbs or spices

Heat the spices and vinegar to 160

degrees F. in a stainless steel or glass pan. Bottle the vinegar and let it cool. No aging is necessary, but if a stronger flavor is desired, age up to 1 month. Strain out the herbs or spices and allow the liquid to stand for a few days. Siphon the clear vinegar off the deposit into sanitized bottles.

EBONY-COLORED WOOD STAIN

This formula blackens wood that contains tannin (oak, cherry, walnut or mahogany).

1 4/0 steel wool pad
2 cups vinegar

Place the ingredients in a glass jar and let them sit for several days or until the steel wool dissolves. To use, sponge the solution evenly onto a sanded wood surface. Allow it to dry overnight. Sand it again and apply a finish.

FABRIC SOFTENER

Add 1/2 cup vinegar to the washing machine's fabric softener dispenser. Vinegar removes yellowing soap scum, making blankets and woolens soft and fluffy.

FRAGRANT TOILET VINEGAR

A mixture of half vinegar and half water has many cosmetic uses. It is a stimulant, astringent and cooling agent to the skin. When used as a hair rinse, it makes hair shine by removing soap residue. A cup of this mixture in a hot bath softens skin. When used as a cool compress, it eases headaches and relieves tension. The acid in vinegar readily dissolves and holds fragrances.

2 cups fresh flowers or herbs,
small amounts of ground spices,
or essential oils
1 tablespoon vodka
Food coloring (optional)

Place the vodka and fragrant material in a quart jar and fill the jar with vinegar. Seal the jar and age it for three weeks in a warm, dark place. Strain out the solids and squeeze the scent material. Wait a few days for the solids to settle. Siphon the clear vinegar off the deposit. Boil an equal amount of water and let it cool. Add the water to the fragrant vinegar.

FRESH FRUIT OR HERB VINEGAR

1 quart vinegar
1/4 cup ripe fruit or fresh herbs

Wash, drain and crush the fruit. Combine the ingredients and heat them to 160 degrees F. in a glass or stainless steel pan. Bottle and seal the warm vinegar. Age it for 1 month in a warm, dark place. Strain it; wait for the solids to settle and siphon the clear vinegar off the deposit into sanitized bottles.

INSECT REPELLENT

1/2 cup vinegar
1 tablespoon camphor
1 tablespoon calcium chloride

Bottle the ingredients. Shake the bottle until the camphor and calcium chloride are dissolved. Rub the repellent over exposed areas of skin. Ingredients are available from "Chem Lab" (see Appendix A). See page 78 for mosquito repellent.

MEAT TENDERIZER

Vinegar marinades are effective meat tenderizers.

MOISTEN-TO-SEAL GLUE

This glue works like that on stamps, labels and envelopes. Moisten it and press together the items to be joined. The essential oil is optional to improve the taste of the mucilage. See page 1 for envelope glue.

6 tablespoons vinegar
1 ounce (weight) unflavored gelatin
    (about 4 small packages)
1 tablespoon essential oil of wintergreen
    or peppermint (optional)

Bring the vinegar to a boil. Add the gelatin and stir until it is completely dissolved. Stir in the essential oil. To use the glue, brush a thin layer on the back of a label, stamp or envelope flap. Let it dry. Moisten the glue and press the items to be joined. The glue will gel and thicken when it gets cold. In the thickened state, it can be used as an ordinary paper paste, or else melt it and use it as a moistening-type glue.

SLUG KILLER

1 measure vinegar
1 measure water

Put the ingredients into a sprayer. Go into the garden after dark and spray the slugs, plants and ground. The slugs die almost instantly and there is no harm to the plants. See page 74 for "Slug Bait".

THIRST QUENCHER

This sweet-tart drink is one of the best thirstquenchers around.

1 tablespoon honey
1 tablespoon vinegar
1 1/2 cups carbonated water

Combine the ingredients and serve it cold.

VEGETABLE VINEGAR

Choose ONE of the following:

- 8 garlic cloves, peeled and crushed
- 1 pound green onions, chopped
- 1 pound sweet peppers, seeded and chopped
- 3 hot peppers, seeded and chopped
- 1 pound sweet onions, peeled and chopped
- 1 pound chopped celery
- 1 ounce (weight) fresh or dry celery seed

Combine the chosen ingredient with 1 quart vinegar containing 7% acetic acid. Heat this to 160 degrees F. Bottle the warm vinegar and age it for 1 month in a warm, dark place. Strain out the solids and allow the liquid to stand for a few days. Siphon or pour the clear vinegar off the deposit into sanitized bottles.

HARD CANDY

2 cups sugar
1/2 cup vinegar
2 tablespoons butter

Combine the ingredients and heat them to 270 degrees F. Pour this onto buttered plates. Mark the candy into squares while it is still warm or roll it into balls.

WINDOW CLEANER

3/4 cup household ammonia
1/4 cup vinegar
3 cups water

Pour the ingredients into a spray bottle and shake well. Spray the window and wipe it clean.

WATERPROOFING

ADDRESS LABELS

Rub a block of pure beeswax over the writing on address labels. Rub the wax with a cloth to smooth it. Although beeswax is yellow, it appears clear over the label. The label is now "rain-proof".

CANVAS TARPAULINS

2 cups boiled linseed oil
2 ounces (weight) beeswax
2 ounces (weight) rosin

Heat the beeswax and rosin in a 250 degrees F. oven until they are melted and combined. Remove this from the oven and stir in the oil. Stretch the canvas and brush on three coats of the warm mixture, allowing one day between coats for the canvas to dry. Tarpaulins covered with this mixture should be hung for storage rather than folded.

CUTTING BOARDS

When cutting boards are wet, the wood fiber swells and frays. Waxing a wooden cutting board waterproofs it and extends the life of the cutting surface. The board must be perfectly dry, clean and smooth. Melt beeswax in a microwave and brush or pour it onto the cutting board. After the wax has cooled, rub over it with an iron set on medium heat. Use cloths or paper towels to wipe off the excess wax.

LEATHER WATERPROOFING

1/4 cup lanolin
2 tablespoons beeswax
2 tablespoons petroleum jelly

Combine the ingredients and melt them in a microwave or a double boiler. Brush the warm mixture over leather. Let this stand for a few hours and polish it with a cloth to remove excess waterproofing. Also see page 46.

WAXED FABRIC CONTAINERS

Inverted baking pans and serving dishes serve as molds to make waxed fabric containers. Food is prepared in the pan and served or presented as a gift in the waxed fabric container.

A waxed-fabric container and the loaf pan used to shape it.

Melt 1 pound beeswax in an oven at 230 degrees F. Invert a mold over waxed paper and spray it with a wax-release agent or vegetable oil. Cut a piece of fabric large enough to cover the mold. Thick fabrics absorb more wax and make sturdier containers than thinner fabrics. Wear rubber gloves and saturate the fabric with melted wax. Before the wax cools, drape the fabric over a mold. When the wax cools, remove the fabric, and trim the edges.

WAX-BLEACHING

Beeswax can be chemically bleached with hydrogen peroxide. This treatment lightens wax considerably, but it also destroys the natural wax aroma. Beeswax for competition in a honey show should never be chemically bleached. Obtain 35% hydrogen peroxide from a laboratory supplier such as "Chem Lab" (see Appendix A) or from a hair styling salon. Wear rubber gloves and eye protection to avoid skin contact with hydrogen peroxide.

Step 1: Pour 1 or 2 inches of 35% hydrogen peroxide into a stainless steel or enamel pot. Estimate beeswax that will equal 2 to 4 inches when it is melted and add it to the pot. The pot should be less than half full to allow room for foaming.

Step 2: Place the pot in an oven set at 225 degrees F. Oven temperatures vary. It is wise to use an oven thermometer and check it often to be sure the proper temperature is maintained. The beeswax will melt and bubbles will begin to come to the surface.

Step 3: Maintain the heat until the bubbles are no longer rising (3 to 4 hours depending on the amount of peroxide).

Step 4: Turn off the heat and wait for the wax to cool. Heat the wax just enough to remove it from the container. Cut off any impurities from the bottom of the wax. The wax takes 2 to 3 days to harden completely.

WOOD FINISHES

The ingredients for these formulas are sold by wood-finishing suppliers such as "Woodworker's Supply" (see Appendix A for suppliers). See page 72 for "Wood Dressing" and page 73 for "Exterior Wood Finish".

FLAT VARNISH

Beeswax causes this interior varnish to dry with a dull luster, rather than a high gloss. This varnish is resistant to heat, liquids and wear. It should be applied directly over shellac or sealer as a single finish coat. Flat varnish is very effective on open-grain, unfilled wood such as oak or walnut. All varnish is slow drying (about 4 hours), so work in a dust-free area.

4 ounces (weight) beeswax
1 quart turpentine
1 gallon varnish

Turpentine and varnish are sold in paint stores. Melt the beeswax in a microwave or double-boiler. Remove the wax from the heat and stir it into the turpentine. Add the wax turpentine mixture to the varnish and stir it well. Strain this through doubled cheesecloth or a nylon stocking. Let it stand for 2 days.

Do not apply varnish during humid weather. Moisture in the air, the brush or the solvent may cause a cloudy area in the finish called "bloom." Stir varnish gently and be careful not to mix in air. Bubbles show as dimples in dried varnish.

OIL AND WAX FINISH (For Bare Wood)

Oil and wax finishes are resistant to impact, heat, alcohol and abrasion. They require much work to apply and long drying periods between coats. Oil and wax finishes are the most beautiful of all wood finishing techniques. Their deep penetration brings out the natural beauty of wood.

Step 1: Make the following formula:

1 ounce (weight) beeswax
1 pint raw linseed oil
1 pint turpentine

Melt the beeswax in a microwave or double boiler. Remove it from the heat and stir in the oil and turpentine. Strain the mixture through doubled cheesecloth or nylon stocking. Let it stand for 2 days. Store the mixture in tightly capped containers to keep the turpentine from evaporating. If the formula becomes gummy during use, stir in a small amount of turpentine.

Step 2: Stain the wood if desired and let it dry at least 2 weeks. Sand lightly with 220-grit sandpaper and remove all dust.

Step 3: Apply a thin layer of the formula with a brush or a rag. Allow this to soak into the wood for 20 minutes. Wipe off the excess with a clean rag. Rub the finish with a cloth, 4/0 steel wool or the bare hand to generate heat and make the finish flow into the pores of the wood. Wipe off any excess and wait 72 hours for the piece to dry.

Step 4: Apply 3 to 6 coats as directed in Step 3, waiting 1 month between each coat. This finish gains depth and luster as more coats are applied.

Step 5: Wax the surface with a good paste wax (see page 79 for "Polish").

WAX FINISH (For Bare Wood)

Wax finishes are created by rubbing coat after coat of wax into raw wood. This method requires the least skill to apply but it is labor intensive. This finish is easy to maintain by adding more wax. It has a rich, soft sheen that is attractive on old pine and primitive furniture. Wax finishes are durable and almost impossible to remove because of the depth to which they penetrate wood.

Step 1: Make the following formula:

6 ounces (weight) beeswax
1/4 cup carnauba wax
1/2 cup turpentine

Melt the waxes in a microwave or double boiler. Remove the wax from the heat and stir in the turpentine. Store this in a tightly capped container.

Step 2: Apply an even coat of wax to the surface with a cloth. Rub hard in circular motions to force the wax into the wood and to bring the wax to a fine polish. If too much wax is applied or if the wax forms lumps on the surface, remove it with 4/0 steel wool that contains a small amount of new wax. Wait 1 week for the wax to harden.

Step 3: Repeat Step 2 as many times as necessary to obtain a fine finish. Allow 6 weeks between successive coats for the wax to harden.

Step 4: Bring the surface to a final high polish with a soft cloth. Maximum pressure is necessary. Wrap a brick in the cloth to provide additional pressure.

WAX FINISH
(For Sealed Wood)

A wax finish is applied faster over sealed wood. Sealing closes pores in the wood. This makes wood less absorbent to wax and permits wax to build up faster on the surface. Varnish, shellac and lacquer are appropriate sealers. This type of finish can be removed since the sealer prevents wax from permeating wood fiber.

Step 1: Stain the wood if desired. Allow 2 weeks for the stain to dry. Sand lightly with 220-grit sandpaper and remove all dust.

Step 2: Seal the wood with a 3-pound cut of shellac. Make this by dissolving 3 pounds bleached shellac into 1 gallon alcohol. Directions for dissolving shellac are written on the shellac container.

Step 3: Sand the seal to level it and remove any shine. Remove all traces of dust and abrasive.

Step 4: Cover the surface with a good paste wax (see page 79 for "Polish"). Allow this to dry for 10 minutes. Rub the wax briskly with a soft, lint-free cloth. Rub in all directions, then rub with the grain of the wood. Wait 72 hours.

Step 5: Repeat Step 4 up to 5 times. Step 4 is best applied by hand, but successive coats may be done with a power polisher.

WAX LACQUER

This lacquer can be used over wood, glass or metal. Parts are by weight.

14 parts shellac
60 parts alcohol
2 parts carnauba wax
1 part beeswax
23 parts turpentine

Heat the shellac and alcohol to 122 degrees F. Melt the waxes and stir them into the turpentine. Heat the turpentine wax mixture to 140 degrees F. Combine all ingredients and stir. Let the mixture cool and strain it through a fine filter or nylon stocking. Let the mixture stand for 2 days before using it.

WOOD FINISH REPAIR

This formula fills dents, holes, bruises, cigarette burns and other imperfections of wood finishes. The hole or damaged area is scraped clean and deepened if necessary to hold the repair formula. This procedure requires skill. Practice on scrap wood before attempting to repair fine furniture.

1/2 ounce (weight) beeswax
2 ounces (weight) shellac

Shellac is sold by "Woodworker's Supply" (see Appendix A). Melt the beeswax and shellac in a small can placed in boiling water. This mixture is used hot. If it is too hot, it boils and burns; if it is too cool, it will react sluggishly. On a metal blade, melt the mixture over a flame. A curved knife or flat-head screwdriver works well. Drop enough of the mixture to fill the hole. Wipe the blade clean. Heat the blade and level the repair.

The repair may be further leveled with fine sandpaper or 4/0 steel wool. Touch-up powder sold by wood-finishing suppliers can be used to match the color of the repair to the surrounding finish. Refinish the area with shellac or varnish and polish with a good paste wax (page 79).

WOOD STAIN--See page 100.

"WORKER BEE"

The "Worker Bee" is an original stuffed doll by the author.

The "Worker Bee" works hard to draw attention to herself. Her costume can be changed to make a "Queen Bee" or "Mr. Drone". No pattern changes are necessary for a queen bee, but a drone's body should be cut wider to make him hefty.

GENERAL DIRECTIONS

Step 1: Obtain the supplies. Enlarge the pattern to the size desired and layout the pieces to determine the amount of fabric required. Do not add a seam allowance.

❑ Good quality felt
❑ Sewing supplies
❑ Movable eyes
❑ Black pipe cleaner
❑ Stuffing
❑ 1/4-inch lace

Step 2: Cut out the pattern. Working with felt simplifies the layout because there is no nap or wrong side.

Step 3: Sew the 3 body pieces together on a sewing machine, using the smallest possible seam allowance. Turn the body so that the raw seams are on the inside. Stuff the body. Hand stitch the top closed by sewing around it and drawing the circle closed.

Step 4: Sew or fuse the face onto one of the head pieces. With the face on the inside and using the smallest possible seam allowance, machine stitch the 2 head pieces to the crown piece. Turn the head so that the raw seams are on the inside. Insert the pipe cleaner. Stuff the head and hand stitch it closed at the neck.

Step 5: Slip stitch the arms and legs. Stuff them. Sew the neck to the body. Sew the arms and legs to the body.

Step 6: Tie a cord tightly around the upper third of the body to create a segment. Make an apron and tie it on.

Step 7: Sew the wings together using the smallest possible seam allowance. Turn them so that the raw seams are on the inside. Stitch the wings onto the back of the body.

Step 8: Glue the eyes and mouth in place. Use 2 French knots to make the nose or paint it. Use gold felt or ribbon to make the body stripes. Sew or glue the stripes in place.

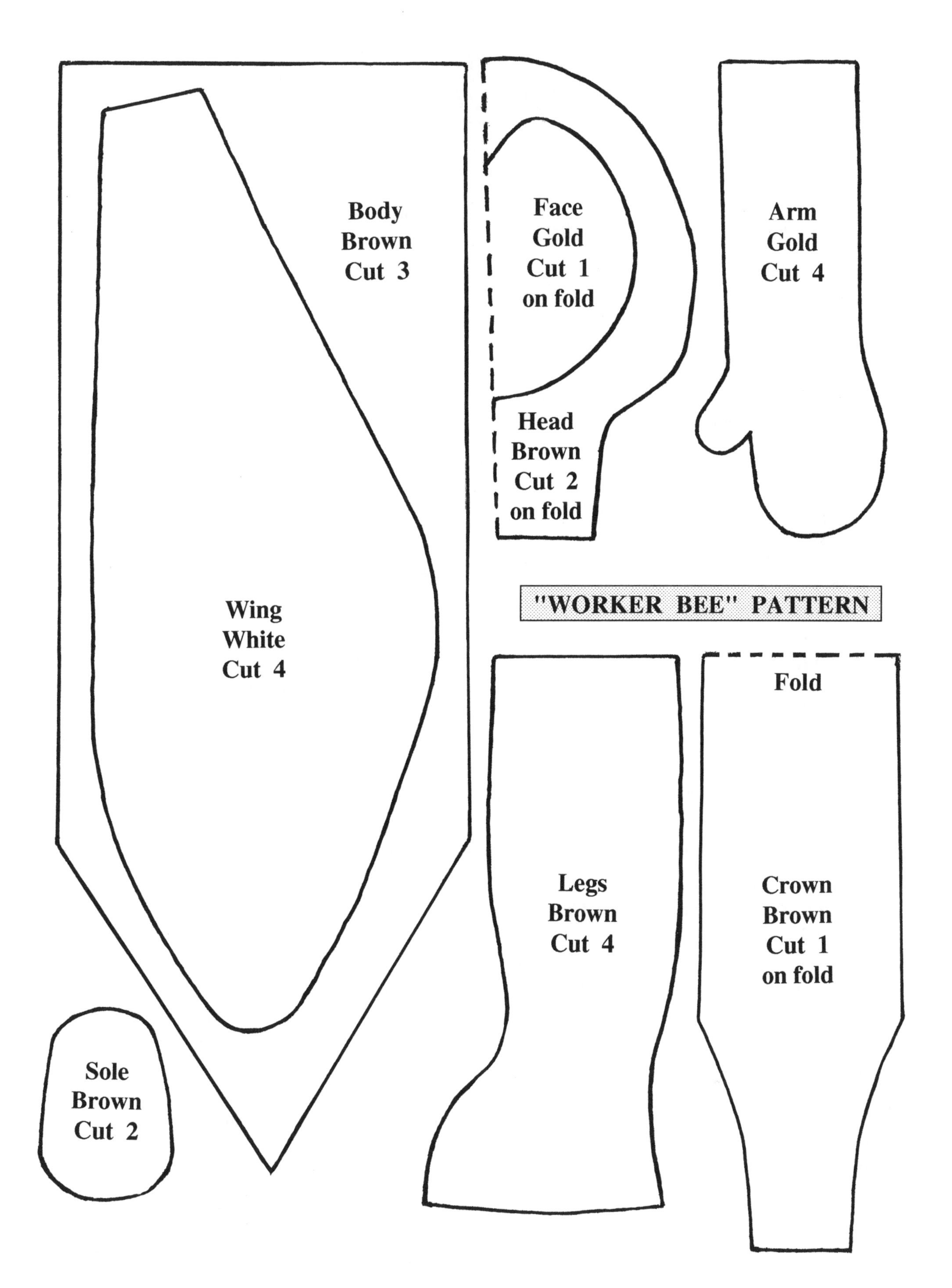
Body
Brown
Cut 3
Face
Gold
Cut 1
on fold
Arm
Gold
Cut 4
Head
Brown
Cut 2
on fold
Wing
White
Cut 4
"WORKER BEE" PATTERN
Fold
Legs
Brown
Cut 4
Crown
Brown
Cut 1
on fold
Sole
Brown
Cut 2

MISCELLANEOUS

ARCHERY WAX

1 ounce (weight) beeswax
1 teaspoon rosin or propolis scrapings

This slightly sticky wax holds bow strings together. Melt the ingredients in a microwave or in a small can placed in boiling water. Pour the wax into a mold and let it cool. Rub bow strings with the block of wax so that heat is generated and the wax adheres.

AUTUMN LEAVES

Gather colorful leaves in the fall before they become brittle. Press them flat in an old book. Set an iron on medium heat. Rub a block of beeswax over the iron and press the leaves to preserve them.

CASTING MEDIUM

1 part by weight plaster of Paris
1 part by weight beeswax

Melt the ingredients together. Stir the mixture and pour it into molds.

CREAM ANTIPERSPIRANT

Add 1 1/2 teaspoons alum to 1/2 cup cold cream or "Ultra-rich Skin Cream", page 89.

DUST MOPS AND DUST CLOTHS

1 tablespoon beeswax (1/2 ounce weight)
2 tablespoons mineral oil
2 cups turpentine

Heat the wax and oil in a microwave or a double boiler until the wax melts. Remove this from the heat and stir in the turpentine. Wet flannel cloth or a dust mop in the liquid. Wring it out and spread it to dry.

GOLF CLUB GRIP WAX

2 ounces (weight) beeswax
1 teaspoon powdered rosin

Melt the ingredients together in a 250 degree F. oven. Pour this into a paper tube. Peel away the paper as the wax is used.

HONEY SUGAR

Capture the essence of honey in the sugar bowl.

1/4 cup honey
2 cups white granulated sugar

Stir the honey and sugar together and spread it thinly over a baking sheet. Place it in a 200 degree F. oven for 25 minutes and stir every 5 minutes. Remove the sugar from the oven and wait for it to cool. Grind the sugar in a blender or a food processor to break up the lumps. Store the sugar in a tightly covered container.

MASSAGE CREAM

The formulation of massage cream is the same as "Skin Cream", page 89. Stir small amounts of liquid soap into the finished cream and test it until the desired "grip" is achieved. To warm skin, add essential oil of sassafras or juniper. To cool skin, add essential oil of wintergreen or peppermint.

MODELING CLAY

Parts by weight:
100 beeswax
75 whiting (calcium carbonate powder)
13 turpentine
7 vegetable shortening or petroleum jelly

Whiting is sold by building supply stores and "Woodworker's Supply" (see Appendix A). Melt the beeswax and shortening or petroleum jelly in a microwave or a double boiler. Remove this from heat and stir in the turpentine. Mix in the whiting until the mixture is dough-like and can be kneaded. Store the clay in a air-tight tin. It will become hard if the turpentine evaporates. Modeling wax formulas are on page 64.

PUTTY

This is a slow-drying putty for filling cracks and nail holes before painting.

1/4 cup linseed oil
2 teaspoons beeswax
Whiting (calcium carbonate powder)

Whiting is sold by building suppliers or "Woodworker's Supply" (see Appendix A). Melt the beeswax in a microwave or a small can placed in boiling water. Add the oil and stir. Heat the mixture again if necessary to get a smooth mixture. Let it cool. Stir in small amounts of whiting until the mixture is dough-like and can be handled. Knead the mixture until it is smooth and store it in an air-tight container.

SORE MUSCLE RUB

2 tablespoons lanolin
2 tablespoons beeswax (1 ounce weight)
1 teaspoon camphor
1 teaspoon oil of eucalyptus
1 tablespoon oil of wintergreen
1 tablespoon menthol

This ointment is good for aching joints and sore muscles. Heat the lanolin and beeswax in a microwave or a double boiler until the wax is melted. Stir in the oils. Continue stirring until the mixture is cold. Ingredients are available from chemical suppliers such as "Chem Lab" (see Appendix A).

SPICE SACHETS

1 1/2 ounce (weight) beeswax
1 cup applesauce
1 1/2 cup ground cinnamon or a mixture of cinnamon, nutmeg, allspice and cloves. Up to 1 teaspoon of essential oil from any of the spices may also be added.

Heat the wax and applesauce in a microwave or a double boiler until the wax is melted. Stir in the ground spices. Knead the mixture until it is dough-like. Roll the dough into sheets and cut out forms or hand-form the dough into balls or beads. Place the forms on cardboard. They will harden in 3 or 4 days. The fragrance will last for years.

STAINED GLASS WAX

4 ounces (weight) beeswax
2 tablespoons turpentine or mineral spirits

Stained glass makers use this adhesive wax to hold copper-foiled glass in place until it can be soldered. Melt the beeswax. Stir in the turpentine and stir until the mixture cools. Knead the wax until it is ductile and sticky. Store it in an air-tight container.

APPENDIX A - SUPPLIERS

A. I. Root Company
(Beekeeping supplies &
Bee Culture magazine)
P. O. Box 706
Medina, OH 44258-0706
1-216-725-6677

Alternative Beverage
(Beer and wine supplies)
114-O Freeland Lane
Charlotte, NC 28217
1-704-527-9643

Apple Acres Apiary
(Bee-related gift items)
P.O. Box 509223
Indianapolis, IN 46250
1-317-849-0678

B & B Honey Farm
(Beekeeping supplies)
Route 2, Box 245
Houston, MN 55943
1-507-896-3955

Barker Enterprises, Inc.
(Candle-making supplies)
15106 10th Avenue, S.W.
Seattle, WA 98166
1-206-244-1870

Beehive Botanicals
P. O. Box 8258
Hayward, WI 54843
1-800-283-4274

Beer & Winemaking
Supplies, Inc.
154 King Street
Northampton, MA 01060
1-413-586-0150

Betterbee Beekeeping and
Candle Supplies (also mead)
Route 4, Box 4070
Greenwich, NY 12834
1-518-692-9669

Brushy Mt. Bee Farm
(Beekeeping supplies)
Route 1, Box 135
Moravian Falls, NC 28654
1-800-BEESWAX

Candlewic
(Candle-making supplies)
35 Beulah Road
New Britian, PA 18901
1-215-348-1544

The Cellar
(Beer and wine supplies)
P. O. Box 33525
Seattle, WA 98133
1-206-365-7660

Chem Lab Supplies
(Laboratory supplies)
1060-C Ortega Way
Placentia, CA 92670
1-714-630-7902

Dabney Herbs
Post Office Box 22061
Louisville, KY 40252
1-502-893-5198

Dadant & Sons, Inc.
(Beekeeping supplies &
The American Bee Journal)
51 South 2nd Street
Hamilton, IL 62341
1-217-847-3324

Daniel Smith
(Art supplies)
4130 First Avenue South
Seattle, WA 98134-2302
1-800-426-7923

Deep Flex Plastic Molds
(Molds and resins)
1200 Park Avenue
Murfreesboro, TN 37129
1-615-896-1111

Doll Gallery
(Doll-making supplies)
1137 Susan Street
Columbia, SC 29210

Doll House Molds
207 McAlpin Street
Duryea, PA 18642
1-717-457-8942

Dover Publications
(Art and craft books)
31 East 2nd Street
Mineola, NY 11501

Draper Super Bee Apiaries
(Beekeeping supplies)
Route 1, Box 97
Millerton, PA 16936-2381
1-800-233-4273

Earth Guild
(Craft supplies)
33 Haywood Street
Asheville, NC 28801
1-800-327-8448

Garrett Wade Co., Inc.
(Woodworking supplies)
161 Ave. of the Americas
New York, NY 10013
1-800-221-2942

Glorybee Bee Box, Inc.
(Beekeeping supplies)
Post Office Box 2744
Eugene, OR 97402
1-800-456-7923

Great Fermentations
(Beer and wine supplies)
87 Larkspur Street
San Rafael, CA 94901
1-415-459-2520

Groeb Farms, Inc.
(Beekeeping supplies)
Post Office Box 269
Onsted, MI 49265
1-517-467-2065

Hagenow Laboratories
(Laboratory supplies)
1302 Washington Street
Manitowoc, WI 54220

Haussmann's Pharmacy
(Herbs & cosmetic oils)
534-536 W. Girard Ave.
Philadelphia, PA 19123
1-215-627-2143

Hubbard Apiaries
(Beekeeping supplies)
Post Office Box 160
Onsted, MI 49265

John Wagner & Sons, Inc.
(Extracts and flavors)
900 Jacksonville Road
Box 5013, Ivyland, PA 18974
1-215-674-5000

APPENDIX A - SUPPLIERS CONTINUED

Lapp's Bee Supply Center
(And candle-making supplies)
Post Office Box 4601
Reeseville, WI 53579
1-800-321-1960

Lavender Lane
(Oils & waxes for cosmetics)
6715 Donerail
Sacramento, CA 95842
1-916-334-4400

Loran Oils
(Flavorings, molds &
candy-making supplies)
Post Office Box 22009
Lansing, MI 48909-2009

Mann Lake Supply
(Beekeeping supplies)
County Rd. 40 & 1st St.
Hackensack, MN 56452
1-800-233-6663

The National Honey Board
(Honey information)
421 21st Avenue #203
Longmont, CO 80501
1-303-776-2337

Nature's Herb Company
(Herb supplies)
1010 46th Street
Emeryville, CA 94608
1-415-601-0700

Penn Herb Company Ltd.
(Herb supplies)
603 North 2nd Street
Philadelphia, PA 19123-3098
1-215-925-3336

Pourette Candle Supplies
P. O. Box 15220
Seattle, WA 98115
1-206-525-4488

The Rosemary House
(Herb supplies)
120 South Market Street
Mechanicsburg, PA 17055
1-717-697-5111

Rosland Farm
(Herb supplies and skeps)
N.C. 82 at U.S. 13
Godwin, NC 28344

Rossman Apiaries, Inc.
(Beekeeping supplies)
Post Office Box 905
Moultrie, GA 31776
1-912-985-7200

Ruhl Bee Supply
(Beekeeping supplies)
12713-B NE Whitaker Way
Portland, OR 97230
1-503-256-4231

The Sausage Maker
(Sausage-making supplies)
26 Military Road
Buffalo, NY 14207
1-716-876-5521

Sax Arts and Crafts
(Everything your art desires)
Post Office Box 51710
New Berlin, WI 53151-0710
1-800-558-6696

Sunburst Bottle Company
($2.00 catalog, containers)
7001 Sunburst Way
Citrus Heights, CA 95621
1-916-722-4632

Sun Feather Herbal Soap
(Soap-making supplies)
HCR 84, Box 60 A
Potsdam, NY 13676
1-315-265-3648

Sunshine Glassworks Ltd.
(Stained glass supplies)
240 French Road
Buffalo, NY 14227
1-716-668-2918

Sunstream
(Beekeeping supplies)
P. O. Box 225
Eightyfour, PA 15330
1-412-222-3330

Surma
(Ukrainian egg supplies)
11 East 7th Street
New York, NY 10003
1-212-477-0729

The Ultimate Collection
(Doll mold catalog $6.00)
12773 W. Forest Hill Blvd.,
Suite 1207
West Palm Beach, FL 33414

Vic's Crafts
(Stained glass supplies)
P. O. Box 1072
Royal Oak, MI 48068

Walter T. Kelly Company
(Beekeeping supplies)
3107 Elizabethtown Road
Clarkson, KY 42726
1-502-242-2012

Wicwas Press
(Beekeeping books)
Post Office Box 817
Cheshire, CT 06410-0817
1-203-250-7575

Woodworker's Supply
1108 North Glenn Road
Casper, WY 82601
1-800-645-9292

New Addresses:

APPENDIX B
TEMPERATURE CONVERSION TABLE

The numbers in bold type (↓) refer to the temperature either in Centigrade or Fahrenheit, which is to be converted into the other scale. If converting from Fahrenheit to Centigrade, the equivalent temperature will be found in the left column. When converting from Centigrade to Fahrenheit, the answer will be found in the column on the right.

C.	↓	F.	C.	↓	F.	C.	↓	F.
-17.80	**0**	32.0	5.04	**41**	105.8	28.00	**82**	**179.6**
-17.20	**1**	33.8	5.60	**42**	107.6	28.56	**83**	181.4
-16.70	**2**	35.6	6.16	**43**	109.4	29.12	**84**	183.2
-16.13	**3**	37.4	6.72	**44**	111.2	29.68	**85**	185.0
-15.58	**4**	39.2	7.28	**45**	113.0	30.24	**86**	186.8
-15.03	**5**	41.0	7.84	**46**	114.8	30.80	**87**	188.6
-14.48	**6**	42.8	8.40	**47**	116.6	31.36	**88**	190.4
-13.93	**7**	44.6	8.96	**48**	118.4	31.92	**89**	192.2
-13.38	**8**	46.4	9.52	**49**	120.2	32.48	**90**	194.0
-12.83	**9**	48.2	10.08	**50**	122.0	33.04	**91**	195.8
-12.28	**10**	50.0	10.64	**51**	123.8	33.60	**92**	197.6
-11.73	**11**	51.8	11.20	**52**	125.6	34.16	**93**	199.4
-11.18	**12**	53.6	11.76	**53**	127.4	34.72	**94**	201.2
-10.63	**13**	55.4	12.32	**54**	129.2	35.28	**95**	203.0
-10.08	**14**	57.2	12.88	**55**	131.0	35.84	**96**	204.8
-9.53	**15**	59.0	13.44	**56**	132.8	36.40	**97**	206.6
-8.98	**16**	60.8	14.00	**57**	134.6	36.96	**98**	208.4
-8.43	**17**	62.6	14.56	**58**	136.4	37.52	**99**	210.2
-7.88	**18**	64.4	15.12	**59**	138.2	38.08	**100**	212.0
-7.33	**19**	66.2	15.68	**60**	140.0	43.64	**110**	230.0
-6.78	**20**	68.0	16.24	**61**	141.8	49.20	**120**	248.0
-6.23	**21**	69.8	16.80	**62**	143.6	54.76	**130**	266.0
-5.68	**22**	71.6	17.36	**63**	145.4	60.32	**140**	284.0
-5.13	**23**	73.4	17.92	**64**	147.2	65.88	**150**	302.0
-4.58	**24**	75.2	18.48	**65**	149.0	71.44	**160**	320.0
-4.03	**25**	77.0	19.04	**66**	150.8	77.00	**170**	338.0
-3.48	**26**	78.8	19.60	**67**	152.6	82.56	**180**	356.0
-2.93	**27**	80.6	20.16	**68**	154.4	88.12	**190**	374.0
-2.38	**28**	82.4	20.72	**69**	156.2	93.68	**200**	392.0
-1.83	**29**	84.2	21.28	**70**	158.0	99.24	**210**	410.0
-1.28	**30**	86.0	21.84	**71**	159.8	104.80	**220**	428.0
-0.73	**31**	87.8	22.40	**72**	161.6	110.36	**230**	446.0
0.00	**32**	89.6	22.96	**73**	163.4	115.92	**240**	464.0
0.56	**33**	91.4	23.52	**74**	165.2	121.48	**250**	482.0
1.12	**34**	93.2	24.08	**75**	167.0	127.04	**260**	500.0
1.68	**35**	95.0	24.64	**76**	168.8	132.60	**270**	518.0
2.24	**36**	96.8	25.20	**77**	170.6	138.16	**280**	536.0
2.80	**37**	98.6	25.76	**78**	172.4	143.72	**290**	554.0
3.36	**38**	100.4	26.32	**79**	174.2	149.28	**300**	572.0
3.92	**39**	102.2	26.88	**80**	176.0	154.84	**301**	590.0
4.48	**40**	104.0	27.44	**81**	177.8	160.40	**302**	608.0

APPENDIX C - CONVERSION TABLES

DRY MEASURE & WEIGHT

From	To	Multiply by
ounces	grams	28.35
pounds	kilograms	0.45
grams	ounces	0.035
kilograms	pounds	2.21

U.S. Regular	Metric
0.035 ounce	1 gram
35.27 ounces	1 kilogram
2.21 pounds	1 kilogram
1/8 teaspoon	0.54 grams
1/4 teaspoon	1.09 grams
1/2 teaspoon	2.19 grams
3/4 teaspoon	3.28 grams
1 teaspoon	4.38 grams
1/8 tablespoon	1.77 grams
1/4 tablespoon	3.54 grams
1/2 tablespoon	7.09 grams
3/4 tablespoon	10.63 grams
1 tablespoon	14.18 grams
1/8 ounce	3.59 grams
1/4 ounce	7.39 grams
1/2 ounce	14.18 grams
3/4 ounce	21.34 grams
1 ounce	28.35 grams
1/8 pound	56.69 grams
1/4 pound	113.39 grams
1/2 pound	226.78 grams
3/4 pound	340.17 grams
1 pound	453.56 grams
1/8 cup	28.34 grams
1/4 cup	56.69 grams
1/2 cup	113.39 grams
3/4 cup	170.08 grams
1 cup	226.78 grams

LIQUID INGREDIENTS

From	To	Multiply by
ounces	milliliters	29.56
pints	liters	0.47
quarts	liters	0.95
gallons	liters	3.78

U.S. Regular	Metric
0.034 ounce	1.00 milliliter
33.81 ounces	1.00 liter
2.10 pints	1.00 liter
1.05 quarts	1.00 liter
0.26 gallons	1.00 liter
1/8 teaspoon	0.61 milliliters
1/4 teaspoon	1.23 milliliters
1/2 teaspoon	2.47 milliliters
3/4 teaspoon	3.70 milliliters
1 teaspoon	4.94 milliliters
1/8 tablespoon	1.84 milliliters
1/4 tablespoon	3.69 milliliters
1/2 tablespoon	7.39 milliliters
3/4 tablespoon	11.08 milliliters
1 tablespoon	14.78 milliliters
1/8 ounce	3.69 milliliters
1/4 ounce	7.39 milliliters
1/2 ounce	14.78 milliliters
3/4 ounce	22.17 milliliters
1 ounce	29.57 milliliters
1/8 cup	29.57 milliliters
1/4 cup	59.14 milliliters
1/2 cup	118.28 milliliters
3/4 cup	177.42 milliliters
1 cup	236.56 milliliters
1 pint	473.00 milliliters
1 quart	946.00 milliliters
1/2 gallon	1.89 liters
3/4 gallon	2.83 liters
1 gallon	3.78 liters

INDEX